COME A LONG JOURNEY

The Yukon River from Whitehorse to Dawson

COME
A LONG JOURNEY

A novel by Alan Fry

Doubleday Canada Limited, Toronto, Ontario
Doubleday & Company, Inc., Garden City, New York, 1971

Library of Congress Catalog Card Number 74–103746
Copyright © 1971 by Alan Fry
Printed in the United States of America
First Edition

By Alan Fry

RANCH ON THE CARIBOO
HOW A PEOPLE DIE

TO THE MEMORY OF CLIVE THOMSON WHO SHARED WITH
ME, IN HIS LAST JOURNEY BEYOND THE BEATEN TRACK
OF OUR FIXED DWELLINGS, MANY CAMPS ALONG THE
YUKON.

ACKNOWLEDGMENT

I am indebted in the making of this story.

I am indebted before everything to the Indian people of the Yukon Territory in ways that become clear, I believe, in the unfolding of this yarn.

And I am indebted to my very good friend, Alan Innes-Taylor of the Yukon Territory, from whom I caught a consuming disease, the only known remedy for which is an endless stretch of a northern river, a strong canoe and an outfit.

PREFACE

As far as the history herein is concerned, I have done my best to be faithful to fact.

But some of the yarns are more folklore than history, and in folklore there may be many versions of an event, factual in itself but remembered by different men in different ways. I have told these the way I heard them, and I beg of those old-timers whose version is different a measure of understanding.

Finally, I want to say of those enchanted hours in a darkened tent in the company of my old storyteller that I was not scribbling away with pencil on paper by candlelight.

I listened. If later in the retelling I have confused a place or a time when something happened, may I be forgiven; for it is his story and what he taught me of men that I have tried to convey here. Yukon Crossing, Little Salmon, Big Salmon: these may not have been the places at all which figured in his trek with the troublesome cheechakos, though this is where my memory has it. But it does not matter.

May you know him through these pages as I did, old now but ageless, endlessly inoffensive, making above all the gift of himself.

The river rises in the glaciers
and the snowpack of the mountains, nurtured
by the storms of the North Pacific Ocean.

She carries away her drainage,
coursing green then silty grey, over gravel
bed and boulder, muddy clay and rotting
snag, moulding a wide valley a thousand
miles to the Arctic, another thousand to
the sea.

She scours at her cutbanks,
erosive and destructive: she nurtures
silty islands, rich in willow growth and
sedge.

She has seen man's long survival
in a cold, forbidding climate. She has
witnessed much of courage and rather more
of folly. She was here before men found
her, she'll be here when they are gone.

Call her the Yukon.

COME A LONG JOURNEY

Chapter 1

There is a backwater in the Yukon River at Whitehorse where the main current, surging over an obstruction on the river bed, leaves at rest a patch of water fed by a gentle reverse flow from the stream.

This is by the disused shipyard of the White Pass and Yukon Route, and you may hold your canoe here in the shadow of three huge and decaying paddle-wheelers, the flat-bottomed ships of the river whose days began with the gold rush and ended with the construction of a highway fifty years later.

Here once, on this same river bank, sweating hands transloaded all the freight—the picks and shovels, the cigars and whiskey, the hymn books and lace curtains, the feathered hats and ladies' stockings, and tons of durable grub—brought in from Skagway at tidewater by the White Pass and Yukon Route Railway, to the decks of the paddle-wheelers and their barges to journey the last four hundred and fifty miles to the Klondike.

It is a good place to tie up your canoe. In a few minutes' walk you have Taylor and Drury's department store where you may still buy most anything for a river trip. If you tell Charlie Taylor, son of a founding partner in this company of traders whose origins also lie in the gold rush, that you are outfitting to go down-river to Dawson City, he will have your grub and gear delivered on the grass beside your canoe, without your telling him where the canoe is tied. River trips, as always, begin at the White Pass yards.

But my canoe was loaded now. I had been the last time to T and D's for some forgotten item, and I stood on the bank with Dave, my Indian companion, sharing the magic moment when everything that preludes a trip has been done. One waits then only

1

to slip out of the world of fixed dwellings, of coming and going by the clock, and meals set on tables, into the peacefully casual and ever-changing life of the river.

Early morning surrounded us. At our backs the town slept and the first light of an autumn sun broke over the mountains to the east.

We had camped here the night before in imitation of the Hudson's Bay start. That Company had made a practice of sending its travelers from the post, before a journey began in earnest, to camp just half an hour from the gates. By morning any missing gear or supplies would be noticed and easily fetched. Men's lives could be saved by that in the north, in winter travel, at sixty degrees below.

But we had no shortages, far from it. I had been so long in camps of all sorts that I was only rarely short of anything.

I had lists, you see. In fact, I had a little book to keep the lists in, lists of every sort for every kind of camp.

I had a canoe list and a Land Rover list, a grub list, a tool list and a dunnage list, one for summer and one for winter. I had a list for going outside, by aircraft to Vancouver, and this included even a white shirt and tie. And I had another list for a survival kit for small aircraft travel in the Territory—fish net and twine, rifle and ammunition, a piece of canvas, some duffle cloth for emergency foot gear, needle and thread, extra moccasins, matches sealed in paraffin.

I carried the little book of lists, amending it from experience. If some supposedly essential object were never used, trip after trip, I would strike it out. Something else, sorely missed, would be added. With a short pencil for the purpose, in my camps in the evenings I would spend time making the changes.

Really rather scientific. Splendid long lists.

Dave had a different way. He didn't spend half his life in camp, he spent the whole of it, and as we looked at the mound of gear stowed under the canvas amidships of my freighter canoe, I would have given up a waterproof container of matches to know his real thoughts.

Once I had met Dave on the river while I was coming up the

2

Thirty Mile from Hootalinqua to Lake Laberge and thence to Whitehorse in a square-sterned canoe with an outboard motor. Dave was traveling down to Hootalinqua and thence to Carmacks in the hope of killing a moose along the way. He and his companion had come overland from Braeburn on the Carmacks-Whitehorse road to Lower Laberge with pack dogs. There they'd cut dry logs and put together a raft, to drift down with the current in the warmth of the sun.

The raft was small and all their outfit took up less space than the two dogs. When Dave, partner, dogs and outfit all gathered on the raft there was room for a moose besides.

I had seen Dave and his partner on the riverbank and had run in to exchange curiosities.

The grin had spread generously over the deep tan creases of his face as Dave had eyed the pile of gear and outfit in the big canoe. Much was fuel, of course, for I was pushing against a stiff current and had no yen to run out of outboard mix then have to drift downstream.

"Whiteman goes some place, he takes hell of a pile of stuff."

Now those were few words, but I missed none of the implication about how lost a whiteman would be without all his stuff, and what would he ever do if he had to leave in a hurry, unable to gather it all up.

So I defended myself as best I could.

"Indian goes some place, he goes tough. Sun shines, mosquitoes eat him up. Rains, he gets washed away. He stays too long and he doesn't kill a moose, he gets hungry." I had a month's supply of grub for a two-week trip and a magnificent tent that kept out mosquitoes or rain with equal proficiency. "Whiteman takes plenty of outfit, stays warm, has good time."

Dave's grin grew bigger. "You goin' watch out in fast water. You get you stuff wet, you boat goin' sink."

So that was how it was with Dave and the big piles of gear essential to the whiteman's way of travel. But Dave and I had become friends and more than once we had shared each other's camps when chance had brought us together somewhere along the roads and rivers of the Territory.

3

Now we were traveling companions, with my outfit, and we had only to step in the canoe and dip our paddles in the ceaseless current to be on the way to Dawson City in the Klondike, those many miles of Yukon River downstream.

So I wondered what Dave thought of all that gear, now he had to help to paddle it as well as share its considerable comfort.

"What you thinking, Dave," I prodded him.

"We goin' be careful how much moose we kill."

I looked fore and aft. We could stow two moose if we boned out most of the meat, three if we camped at the kill long enough to dry some of it.

"C'mon now, we got lots of room. How many moose you figure to kill?"

Dave avoided the question. "You keep you big gun close by. We have to shoot him while we still upriver. We get downriver, we never get back up." Dave meant my 'scope-sighted .270. It reached four times as far as his ancient carbine and had probably killed ten times less meat.

A shrewd winner while ahead, Dave cast off and stood by forward, assuming I'd want him to paddle bow.

I did. He could watch the water for himself and make signals back to me when he thought we should cross the current for any reason.

I made myself comfortable astern. Dave pushed out, stepping aboard in an easy movement and soon the current caught us. We brought her about in the stream, falling into the easy stroke that gives control to the canoemen but leaves the work to the river.

We were in no rush. Life is for living. The river is for traveling. There is no hurry essential to either.

Chapter 2

Against the cutbanks on the outside of the curves, the river throws her greatest volume and velocity. Here the current is swift, the water deep.

Across on the inside of the same curve the current slows and the settling debris forms bars that reach out into the stream, putting riffles on the surface of the water.

Often, the eroding cutbank and the pursuing bar move so far across the valley they let the river rage across the bar in a straight new path at floodtime, cutting off the land that penetrated so far into the outward curve, making an island.

Now the island becomes its own kind of obstruction, splitting the current, gathering an upstream bar and a downstream bar of its own, adding to its length and paying the price of a new cutbank forming on its fresh new side.

To the man who understands her, to a man like Dave, the river tells much to aid his travel.

Primarily, before all else, active erosion on the cutbank side, on the long outside course of the outward curve, bespeaks deep water and fast current.

Here, in the main, lies the course of all river vessels: the paddle-wheeler, for of course she needs the draft; the powered canoe or river skiff, because the outboard propellor projects below the keel, exposed to the lurking gravel bars; and the paddled canoe, for she seeks the faster water rather than the shortest distance, though not so persistently as the others. Indeed, sometimes the course across the bars suits her well.

So, mainly, the riverman seeks the cutbank, cutting across the stream from side to side with the current, picking up each new cut far enough downstream of its beginning to avoid the bar above.

But it is not always so straightforward. Here a bar has formed under the very ledge of the cutbank and only the slightest riffle gives it away.

Suddenly, on the crossing to the cutbank next downstream, a bar reaches out at right angles where it has no business. But as suddenly, one sees the spot, right next to the bank, not twenty feet across, where half the river is boiling through, where the room is, if only one can reach it before sweeping onto the gravel.

And this other place, here, where the whole river sprawls into a fearful width, dissipating all her water into fiddling little streams, ribboned between a hundred half-seen beds of muck and gravel, great uprooted trees lying about, their trunks imbedded in the bars, their roots reaching through the surface, collecting more silt, compounding the maze.

Where do you look for the main current and the deep channel here? How many seasons on the river does it take to train an eye that instinctively picks this one exposed bar, not greatly different from the rest in all this desolation, but which allows next to it the one erosive surge of water that has the depth the craft so badly wants?

Indeed, how many seasons; and how agreeable to have Dave in the bow.

But the river is kind below Whitehorse and as far as the mouth of Laberge. We slipped along midstream, then left to a cut and soon right. A shift in the paddle stroke made the changes, called for by the current, silently agreed without words, sometimes prompted by a raised paddle or a half-pointed arm from Dave.

The sibilance of water surging and the lapping dip of the paddles became the background sound against which everything else must now be heard: the whistling of ducks' wings, the slap of a beaver's tail; eventually, the loud splashing of a moose in hasty alarm.

It is thirty miles from Whitehorse to the mouth of Lake Laberge and half way there the Takhini River comes in from the west, dumping her muddy silt into the glacier-fresh waters of this lake-fed stretch of the Upper Yukon. But now, by mid-September, the Takhini too is clear, and only a shadowy line separates the different waters as the streams converge.

We passed the mouth of the Takhini a little beyond midmorning. By noon we had only the last bends of the river above Laberge before us.

Lake Laberge is seldom still. She is thirty miles long, lying dead straight in the north-south of the valley. The winds blow straight down from the south or up from the north, and most of the time they blow hard, gusting to gale force.

In a thirty-mile fetch, this builds a steep, fast sea fit to swamp a flat-bottomed river skiff or put a canoe and the men who handle her to all the test they want.

On a north wind, wise men, sizing up the breakers over the shallow waters of the river mouth, put to shore in time. On a south wind, they may follow the wind down the east shore to the deserted Indian village of Upper Laberge to wait for quieter water. Or if they think their boat can handle it, they might take the west shore to Richtoffen Island then cross the lake and run before the wind to Lower Laberge.

Men have died from misjudging Lake Laberge.

We came in on a south wind. It had been blowing all through the late morning, rattling the aging aspen leaves on the lower slopes, bending the trees on the exposed ridges.

Now, as we opened up the lake around the last turn, then rode the current to the last cutbank on the east shore, we saw the darkness of the water in the distance where, after the first mile of fetch, the wind had room to build a choppy sea. Beyond, we made out the white caps of cresting waves.

We ran down the wind to the beach below Upper Laberge, taking the canoe in on the shingle.

Dave made fast to a drift log, while I walked about to work the stiffness of the long sit in the canoe out of my legs.

The sun was bright in the unusually clear air, and its September warmth still had the strength to invite a man to stretch and laze. When the stiffness had worked out, I sat with my legs out on the beach, my back against the drift log.

7

Dave watched the lake a while, then joined me at the log.

"Maybe it blows for a week," I suggested.

"Oh, he might," Dave agreed, the way he'd agree to most anything. The trader might forget you owed him four hundred dollars on last winter's credit or you might shoot a moose trying to climb into your meat cache, but generally there is a pattern to events you may rely on. "South wind lets up every little while. North wind blows, she blows maybe four, five days 'n you stay one camp all time."

"So we better have lunch, in case we get a chance to go all of a sudden."

Dave responded by gathering twigs and small driftwood. By the time I had the cold bannock out and a billycan of water from the lake, he had a fire blazing.

I fed myself cold bannock with one hand while I hung the billy in the fire by a hooked branch with the other. The enveloping flames surrounded the billy, boiling the water in moments. We had tea with the next piece of bannock.

When the meal was done, we picked a way through the willows that overhung the beach to the remains of the old village. Perhaps a dozen cabins still stood in an uneven row, sixty yards or more back from the bank. An occasional cache building, careening on its uprights, stood near the cabin to which it belonged. Farther back, overgrown by the aspens and willows, lay the remains of a few other buildings.

Rags and bottles and rusty coal-oil cans lay where the villagers had tossed them in the careless way of Indian people—not careless in that they should have been tidy but weren't, but in that they really didn't care in the way the whiteman does. Their litter shares their yard with them. It is not in their values that it shouldn't. After twenty years of desertion an Indian village remains obviously Indian by its litter alone, if nothing else.

These dwellings had been built around the turn of the century and later, after gold rush. A whiteman, giving up the pursuit of gold, had taken a wife here; he had shown the people how to build more adequate cabins than their earlier huts; his daughter in Whitehorse proudly remembers how her father had cooked whiteman's food for the people and shown them how to use the tools and gear that gold rush brought in such immense quantity to the Yukon.

He had been a good whiteman. He had lived out his life with his wife's people, caring for her and caring for them. He had received letters from his relatives somewhere back in the United States, and had replied. But he never deserted his new people, as so often the early whitemen did, taking Indian women as a convenience while they were in the country, leaving them and the country together after tiring of it all in a few years.

My mind turned from the whiteman then to the legendary Indian whose people the whiteman had shared.

"Jim Boss used to be Chief here," I said to Dave.

"Yeh. He buried across the lake, by Shallow Bay."

There was a sackful of stories around about Jim Boss. Imagination aside, he'd been quite a man.

Jim Boss, the stories have it, ran Upper Laberge the way he saw fit, prior to, at the time of and following the great influx of '98. He owned this end of Lake Laberge, if indeed he didn't own it all, and one large swipe of the river valley upstream to the south. He owned it the only way you owned anything in those days, by being there first and hanging on.

He ran the first toll system in the Territory. When Indians of other bands came through on the waterway with furs or the trade goods to barter for furs, Jim Boss gave them the unimpeded use of his waterway—for a price, in furs or goods.

When the Ninety-Eighters went through, Jim extended the system, and more than one gold seeker lightened his load a little at the entrance to Lake Laberge.

Well, even such legendary people as Jim Boss grow old and die. When Jim seriously approached the age for it, the whiteman had been in the country for quite a few years, the Indians had taken most of his goods and some of his customs into use, and Taylor and Drury in Whitehorse were doing business in everything from cradles to coffins.

The northern Athabascans of the southern Yukon put much

9

stock in the ceremonies of death. Feasting and gift-giving, tribute and display marked the burial of an important man.

So heavily did these requisites weigh on the mind of men of position that often they saved everything they had a chance to earn in the last years of life, existing the while frugally and in hardship so that they might die certain of a splendid burial.

Jim Boss had position and the means to maintain it, so he decided he'd have himself the finest last-time box ever to be stowed away under a grave house.

Catching the boat going upstream to Whitehorse one day, he called on his friends at the Taylor and Drury post. He explained what he wanted and they showed him the stock. There were some mighty impressive caskets, but they didn't measure up.

Jim explained that he wanted a last-time box to beat all last-time boxes, and that he had accumulated the wealth to pay for it. Taylor and Drury didn't doubt that. Jim was a good customer.

The catalog came out and Jim selected the most magnificent and expensive last-time box Taylor and Drury had ever ordered. They would never have stocked it, and there are few customers for caskets who come in to make their own selection ahead of time.

The order went out over the rails of the White Pass and Yukon Route Railway to Skagway then down the coast to Seattle. Then back by the same route came the casket, carefully crated against the hazards of travel over the sea and through the mountains.

Word went down the river to Upper Laberge that the casket had arrived. Jim came to inspect.

It *was* magnificent. Gold-washed handles graced the sleek quilted sides. The lid, draped generously with silks, raised silently on hand-polished hinges. Inside, the softest lining, in hues of white with a hint of blue, waited to carry off the remains of at least a prince or a bishop.

Jim was pleased. He grinned happily at the storekeepers and his retinue of friends who'd come up from Laberge. Here indeed was a last-time box for the man who still undoubtedly owned Lake Laberge and a big swipe of the river, even though now he generously consented to share it with the White Pass boats, without toll.

Well, the Company would be glad to store the box carefully until it was needed, and did Jim want to pay for it now or later?

Jim thought that over then decided there was just one further thing.

What was that? The firm of Taylor and Drury was anxious to please.

A man should try out his last-time box, just to be sure it was right in every respect.

Well, anything for a customer, so old Jim climbed in and someone closed the lid ever so gently so Jim could get the whole feel of the thing.

Then in a moment, up with the lid and out with old Jim.

It was out with old Jim all right, agitated as a grizzly bear being pestered at a kill by a wolverine.

He spluttered, his English worse than ever. But the storekeepers calmed him down at last. Whatever was wrong, they said, they'd surely be able to fix it.

"She all dark in 'ere!" he exclaimed at last. "Can't see a goddam thing!"

Someone was resourceful enough for any situation. "Why, we'll put windows in her for you, Jim. Best windows you could want."

Jim was struck happy again, completely happy. He knew enough about last-time boxes to know his would be the only last-time box anywhere in the Yukon, below the ground or above it, with windows in it.

So Taylor and Drury hired the best carpenter in Whitehorse, who carefully installed windows in the casket. The upholstery was adjusted, and you would never know that everything hadn't been just so designed from the start. Jim tried it out again to his utter satisfaction, paid for it and left it in Taylor and Drury's care for the time when he would need it.

That time came and one of the North's great individualists was buried on the shores of Lake Laberge, the lake he owned, in the last-time box of his choice.

And through the years that story has been told with much amusement, as the measure of the foolishness of an illiterate and ignorant old man.

But some say there was no smirking when Jim, in pursuit of something important to himself and to his people, did what mattered to him.

The carpenter, they say, did not laugh, at Jim's expense, when called upon to install windows in a coffin. He applied the skills of his trade to doing a proper job.

Chapter 3

The wind died down in a couple of hours, so suddenly that we scrambled to put out, rigging a canvas to catch what we could of the dwindling following breeze.

With the September darkness closing early, we knew we couldn't make the end of the lake, so we set on reaching some small stream mouths on the east side where the rising bulwarks of granite give up a little space—enough to pitch a decent camp.

We came to a site we liked about an hour before dusk and put in.

When men of long experience afield travel together, they quickly fall into a system of making and breaking camp. Everything is done in the most convenient order and the work is divided by each man's aptitudes. Thus, the effort to maintain shelter and warmth and prepare food is both kept to the minimum and also made enjoyable. And all without words, words better used later for telling bear stories over the second billy of tea.

Perhaps nothing tries the cheechako, the tenderfoot, on the trail more than the effort just to stay alive: making camp in the wrong places, often in the dark, eating burned or half-cooked food, ending up wet, cold and hungry in spite of putting in three times the time and effort he can really spare to avoid it.

He chooses rough ground because he waited too late to stop, and there seems nothing better left. As darkness gathers he props his tent awkwardly, anxious to get on with a meal.

The meal is tolerable only because of his hunger. Canned food sticks to the pan he leaves momentarily in a flaming fire while he wipes tears from smoke-filled eyes.

Because the billy stick wasn't secure, the tea billy spills, putting out the fire. It is ages before he has it going again.

Exhausted, he goes to bed but sleeps hardly at all. The rough ground yields no comfort, and it is beyond him now to cut boughs enough to cushion it. Those he did cut were too coarse, and he laid them the wrong way up. They poke him now as he rolls about searching for comfort.

It rains, and the tent leaks where the foot of his sleeping bag has pushed against it in his struggles. The bag is soaked for a quarter of its length before he knows what is happening.

Morning finds him weary, yet somehow he must eat, dry his outfit, roll it all and get on his way. Some days it seems he hardly travels at all, spending all his time in the agonizing business of making and breaking camp and trying to conjure up decent meals, occasionally attempting to go without them altogether.

Even when camping together for the first time, it is effortless for old hands to divide the work and quickly get through to the leisure of a good camp. Within two camps made and broken, they will know each other's ways as if they'd been trail partners for a lifetime.

So, to my relief, it seemed to have happened with Dave and myself.

Dave tied the canoe by a long line up from the beach, then we both surveyed the ground. Here, where the beach gave way to a low bank, was just the level ground we needed.

Two small aspens wanted chopping out, flush to the sod. In a moment it was done.

Since it was my outfit, I fetched the tent to the site, then the poles, then set to marking off the ground.

Meantime, Dave unloaded the canvas bags marked grub and the canvas bags marked cooking gear, piling them to hand.

By the time I had the base tripod up, Dave had the stove on the site and a pile of wood beginning to grow.

Then when the remaining poles went in, filling the teepee out and making a home out of a bundle of canvas, Dave had the bedding on hand and the remaining gear—packboards, spare rope, ex-

14

tra canvas, a bit of fishing tackle—all tucked back under a tarpaulin in the canoe for the night.

Sixteen feet across the base, my teepee offered an abundance of room and comfort to two men. With the help of the bundle of light dry poles, which fitted easily into the load on the freighter canoe to save me cutting fresh ones at each camp, I could have the tent up and the fire going within twenty minutes of clearing the campsite, leaving time for lounging, each man on his own side of the roaring stove, the tea billy boiling, and all the grub and utensils to hand at the back.

Apart from our dry run at the White Pass yards the night before, this was our first camp made together and with the teepee up we both stood back to look.

"Well, what do you think, Dave?"

Dave made practical use of the standard low-walled A-frame tent so widely found throughout the north; and indeed properly used it does all a tent must do for the man in the bush. But it offers less luxury than the teepee.

"He's good tent," he said at last. "Nice tent for sittin' around, too."

So, quickly we laid the bedding out, stowed the grub, then lit the fire. Soon the billy boiled, the tea leaves were in, and while we sipped the first hot mugs of brew, chunks of beef and gravy simmered hot in the frying pan to spill over steaming rice: not moose meat yet perhaps, but worthy of the camp, just the same.

Darkness fell. The air turned cold with the night and we stoked the stove against it, making it fearfully hot inside the tent, but comforting and secure. A candle stuck on a pot lid threw a soft yellow light over the jumble of gear.

Dave, lying on his side with a forearm propping his head, facing the heat of the stove, began to talk a little of his simple interests, of animals and men, the seasons and his travels, of grub and hardship and traders whose credit was much disliked and too much used.

How little I really knew him. I couldn't recall when I'd first met him, but it must have been early in my time in the Yukon. And there had grown then one of those casual associations, promoted

15

as much by chance as anything, in which you wonder later how or why it started. Having happened to meet him a few times, I began to call at his winter camp on the Whitehorse to Carmacks road when my travels took me by.

I liked old Dave and I guess he liked me, and here we were. Just that simple and yet not quite simple. Sometimes one is caught in an association reminiscent of growing up: it becomes important to be more than just liked.

One seeks acceptance, and perhaps the hardest part is knowing when it's there.

Chapter 4

How long is long ago?

The question leaves you puzzling where the thread of beginning lies.

Long ago is the time when the animals looked and talked like men; when Animal Mother put the animals one by one in her swing, giving Caribou the antlers that had belonged to Rabbit; when Raven guiled Beaver Man for a lump of mud, shaping out of it the earth—the mountains and the valleys, the hills and the far away land.

Long ago the land stretched unbroken across what is now the Bering Strait, and a succession of many little bands of nomadic hunters found their way out of Asia into a new world, not knowing where they went, traveling not only by snowshoe and toboggan, skin boat and raft, but by generations, the son going a little farther than the father, the grandson a little farther yet.

Long ago the first of them came, and if we should ever reckon when, we shall count it in millennia.

Long ago the first who came had long since gone to the farthest reaches of two continents, from the top half to the bottom half of the world.

Long ago came the last but one, the Athabascan-speaking peoples. And we do not guess how long in years but long enough, we know, to occupy the whole of the Boreal forest and part of the barren lands clear to Hudson's Bay.

So, long before the memory of a people whose stories are recorded only by the listening of the young to the old, there were Athabascans in the interior of the southern Yukon.

They survived in a harsh climate in little scattered hunting groups, perhaps loosely allied into bands, gathering at some seasons, dispersing at others. Dialects might be kept alive with fewer than fifty speakers.

More in common than anything else among them was the technology by which they survived: the snare, small enough for the ground squirrel or large enough for the moose; the bow and arrow, tipped with fire-hardened antler or finely chipped stone; the snaring wing, a long brush fence with few "escapes" for the caribou or sheep driven against it, each set with a snare; the pound, a corral led to by concealed wings of log and brush through which the animals would be driven by a fleet handful of hunters, who would close in to slaughter only in the concentration of the entrapment itself; the deadfall; the snowshoe of wooden frame filled with thongs of rawhide; the fish trap of driven stakes in the narrow stream, contrived to invite entry, forbid escape; the fish net in a larger stream or lake, meshed with twine spun and laid by hand from fibers found in willow bark; the boat of skins over a lashed wooden frame; the raft of logs controlled by sweeps in the swift current of the rivers; the cooking pot of bark brought to the boil with hot rocks; the paunch of the moose used as a steam kettle, hung near the flames by a soaked thong which turned the suspended weight for even cooking as it slowly dried; the bone needle and awl; the sinew thread; the clothes of tanned hides, especially the winter fur garments, and the mitts and moccasins against the bitter cold; the carefully dried moss, soft and absorbent, to catch the infant's wastes; the quickly contrived shelters of a people who must ever move in search of food in an unforgiving land; and above all the gathered knowledge of where and when to kill the game, catch the fish, gather and preserve the berries, dig the roots and seek the moss beneath the snow when starvation threatened.

On the coast, a few days' walk through the mountain passes, were another people, the Tlingit, whose language could only be distantly related if at all to the Athabascan tongues, and whose technology differed as the sea and the tide beach do from the Boreal forest and the subarctic valleys.

When history begins in the ancestral memory of the people of

18

the interior and the coast, it embraces their relationship, telling of the trade in abalone shell and mountain-goat wool, of the traffic up the coastal rivers to the divide, even of the shifting of people in and out of the interior.

But it is threaded in and out with myth and is not exact. The Tlingit-speaking people at Teslin Lake are truly Tlingit, having come up the Taku River and over the divide by Nakina. But what of the Tlingit-speaking Tagish at Old Caribou Crossing, whom we take as an Athabascan people so dominated by the Tlingit in trading days that they gave up their own language in favor of the other?

In the main, however, the interior belonged to the Athabascans and the coast to the shrewd and scheming Tlingit, whose tribes were highly organized into the elaborate clans and kinship affiliations of the northwest seaboard.

Then the whitemen arrived.

They came to the coast in ships, and the first among them were the Russians, who explored the coast of Alaska in the second of Bering's voyages in 1741.

Bering died in the wreck of his vessel, but surviving sailors took sea otter pelts, obtained by trading, to Petropavlovsk, starting a fur traffic that altered the life of the Indians of the northwest coast and the interior of the Yukon and Alaska forever.

The hunger of man, from the legitimate hunger of the hunter to the greed of the princes of trade, is endless. By the end of the century, Spanish, British, American and French vessels had all been to the coast, forcing the trade into bitter intensity.

The white traders prospered and the Tlingit prospered, but the sea otter, lowly mammal of the northern Pacific, did not. Slaughtered for his pelt, the foundation of the trade, his numbers diminished until neither white hunter nor Tlingit could kill enough in a season to satisfy the hunger of the trader for a greater profit and that of the Tlingit for a better potlatch.

The Tlingit turned to the interior where the hunger of the foreigners, the Athabascan speakers, for beads and knives made them eager to be drawn into the traffic.

19

Profits were enormous. The Tlingit had no way of knowing the value beyond the seas of the interior pelts they delivered to the whitemen at a price in trade goods on their own coast, but it mattered little. The Athabascans, in turn, knew nothing of prices on the coast, and they set their deadfalls in earnest. All the furs a man could catch in a winter might buy a knife, as much again an axe.

The Tlingit became traders, avaricious middlemen, pursuing their craft with ingenuity and determination.

They packed their trade goods into the interior on their backs and the backs of their slaves, bringing out the harvest of furs in the same way.

They guarded the passes solidly against intrusion by non-Tlingit, white or Indian. The simple people of the interior and the trails that reached them belonged to the Tlingit, and the Tlingit had a highly aggressive possessive instinct.

For many decades, no one attempted the passes. There were other routes to the interior and haltingly these were tried.

In 1833 the Russians established St. Michaels at the mouth of the Yukon River, two thousand miles from the same headwaters reached in a few days' walk by the Tlingit packers. From this base the Russians traded up the river for all of a decade, but they did not penetrate what is now Yukon Territory.

In 1847, Alexander Murray of the Hudson's Bay Company came over to the Porcupine from the posts on the Mackenzie. Descending to its mouth on the Yukon, he established Fort Yukon in Russian territory.

In 1848 Robert Campbell, also adventuring and trading for the Bay, came from the Mackenzie by the Liard River and Frances Lake, over the divide into the headwaters of the Pelly. From there he descended the Pelly, building Fort Selkirk at its mouth on the Yukon.

And the Hudson's Bay Company did not realize that these two posts were on the same long watercourse.

Fort Selkirk consisted of the meagerest living quarters and a cache building for trade goods and fur. The precious space in the canoes and packs, which were the means of transport between the distant posts on the Mackenzie and Fort Selkirk at the Pelly mouth, was not intended to bring comfort to the man who occupied the outpost.

This was nothing to Robert Campbell. With the dedication given by so many men to that thankless company, Robert Campbell, who had once eaten the babiche in his snowshoes, set out to win the trade of the southern Yukon for the counting houses of London.

But he was too close to the Tlingit to succeed, only three hundred miles from their passes to the south. In 1852 they burned his few buildings, his supplies and outfit. He retreated up the Pelly, across the divide, back to the Mackenzie and then snowshoed across half a continent, to St. Paul, to secure permission to rebuild. But the Bay was done with the southern Yukon and would not return until others broke the way.

Fort Yukon survived a little longer, for it lay beyond the reach of Tlingit interest. But in 1867, the Americans bought Alaska from the Russians and insisted on the relocation of the post out of their new territory. The Bay relocated upstream once more, then deserted the area altogether when they found they hadn't moved far enough and were still in American territory.

So for most of a century, the wily Tlingit had the trade of the southern interior of the Yukon and most particularly of the people upstream of the Pelly mouth to themselves.

But if those who had come for fur found the permanent penetration of the interior against the wishes of the Tlingit and the immensity of communication and supply too much at the price, those who sought gold did not.

Men who had sought the yellow treasure from California to Barkerville in the Cariboo and who had seen the last days of many camps sensed that farther north in the great backbone of the Americas there should be another big strike, another mining camp, one more chance to swarm in the way of the miner and the barkeep, the claim jumper and the dance-hall girl.

In 1873 Arthur Harper, veteran of the Fraser, found his way in by the Mackenzie and the northern divide. For better than twenty years he lived on the river, mostly alone, poling up and drifting down, searching the side streams, seeking the gold but never finding more than wages.

In 1878 George Holt, little known but for this one feat, somehow got past the Tlingits and reached the interior through the southern passes, and came out with two impressive nuggets traded from an Indian "in Alaska."

In 1880 hard-rock gold was discovered halfway down the panhandle and Juneau sprang up, collecting a crowd of prospectors and frontiersmen, whose one enduring characteristic was that they had to keep moving.

After Juneau there was only the interior left.

So, finally the insistent search for treasure broke the hold of the Tlingit. Influenced by the presence of an American gunboat, these crafty traders, cornered by events, finally let the prospectors through.

This penetration gained momentum slowly. Those who came through the passes did not at first travel far below the headwaters: thousands of miles away at the mouth the very length of the river dissuaded more than a handful from penetrating into the unknown land.

As the numbers grew, as the slow, persistent traffic of the poling boats and rafts began to swell in search of treasure, some few turned to trade; to trade in the outfits the miners must have, to trade in the flour and beans on which men kept alive, to trade with the natives they found there for the fur that was no longer the private preserve of the Tlingits.

Harper was one of these; so too were Al Mayo and Jack McQuesten, men whose time in the north was already long and whose patient faith that somewhere treasure waited to be found kept others searching after they themselves had become storekeepers.

The Yukon became their only home. They took Indian wives, treating them well. They traded as partners at times, and sometimes separately. Often they traded as agents for the Alaska Commercial Company, but usually as private traders. Their first post, Fort Reliance, became the base of exploration.

Tributary rivers were called after their distance from Fort Reliance: joining downstream the Twelvemile and the Fortymile, upstream the Sixty Mile. Unnoticed was the Klondike itself, a scant six miles upstream, where in a few short years the frenzy of Dawson City would have bursting life and then long decline.

Their steamer, the New Racket, worked up and down the long reach of the river from the mouth bringing in supplies. It was the forerunner of fleets of wood-burning, steam-powered paddle-wheelers that would take over the whole length of the river from Whitehorse Rapids to St. Michaels in the years to come.

The prospectors found gold prior to the big strike. By 1886 the men trekking in by the Chilkoot Pass had come on the Stewart River perhaps two hundred strong. In one year they panned out a hundred thousand dollars in fine placer gold.

McQuesten built a post at the mouth of the Stewart on the Yukon, and Stewart was born.

No sooner was that done than on the encouragement of Harper coarse gold was panned out of the Fortymile.

The men on the Stewart left their diggings, heading downriver to the new strike. The town of Forty Mile came into being, hacked out of the wilderness like its predecessors, full of promise, destined to live its short life, unknowing of its fate, to be cut dead by a newer and greater strike, just as it had bled the camps of the Stewart.

In 1893, downriver again in Alaska, another strike and another town, this time Birch Creek and Circle City, another McQuesten town this one, bolted out of the gold pans into existence.

And Circle City lived big and rowdy after the fashion of the American West, while Forty Mile settled down to the law and order of British territory and the Northwest Mounted Police.

Unknowing, men were swept through the succession of events that culminated in the big strike on the Klondike and the upheaval of '98.

In 1894, having been up the Pelly and having found no gold, a man who'd spent a lifetime seeking the biggest of all strikes drifted back down the Yukon. Robert Henderson was his name, a hardy Nova Scotian.

He came to the mouth of the Sixty Mile where, on an island at a place they called Ogilvie, Harper and Ladue (Ladue being a fourth man to join the fluctuating association of these trader-outfitters) had a trading post and sawmill.

Henderson had about had his fill, but on the enthusiasm of Ladue, who was prepared to grubstake him to one more try, he agreed to prospect the Indian River and its tributaries another few miles down the Yukon on the east bank.

For two seasons Henderson scoured the creeks of the Indian River country, and in the second season he crossed the summit to the next drainage north.

There he hit a promising prospect on a creek he called Gold Bottom, a prospect that gave him eight cents to the pan, a good prospect in the bread-and-butter creeks that lure a man on.

He reckoned the creek must drain into the river the men on the Yukon knew as the Klondike, some fifty-five miles downstream of the mouth of the Sixty Mile River and Ladue's post, and forty-five miles upriver of Forty Mile, now the administrative center of this infant territory.

Henderson persuaded several men working the Indian River to join him, and as the season went on their prospects became promising. Finally, with several hundred dollars from their efforts, Henderson went back over the divide to the Indian River, down to the Yukon and up to Ladue's post at Ogilvie for supplies.

There he passed the word, in the tradition of the prospector, of the find on Gold Bottom and how to reach it.

But when he returned he chose another route—down the Yukon and up the Klondike.

Thus he had an encounter (the subject of controversy to this day) with a man of an utterly different nature to himself, one George Carmack.

George Carmack was an American drifter who'd jumped ship in Juneau and ended up in Dyea, in Tlingit country at the foot of the passes, and who'd found the Indians more congenial than his fellow whitemen.

And he must have found the Tagish of the interior more congenial than the Tlingit, for by the middle of the last decade of the nineteenth century, when all men now moved freely through the passes, he had pretty much adopted the life of the Tagish Indians.

24

He had married a Tagish woman, and he traveled the river in the easy and speculative way of his Indian companions, hunting here, drying fish there, aloof from the increasing fever of the prospectors.

Unlike the earlier men who had taken Indian wives and taught them to live as whites, he had taken an Indian wife and chosen to live as an Indian.

He wasn't a prospector, and it was in keeping with his chosen way of life that when Bob Henderson came to the mouth of the Klondike that day in August of 1896, he found Carmack there in camp with his Tagish companions drying fish.

But it was in keeping also with Henderson's code that he passed on word to Carmack of the strike on Gold Bottom. The point is disputed, but in Carmack's version Henderson also cautioned that while there was room for Carmack he didn't want any damn Siwashes staking on the creek.

In no great rush—Carmack lacked the fever of the true prospector—but in a few more days, he and his companions made their way to Gold Bottom and Henderson's camp.

It was a promising prospect, but a hard one to work and no one would get rich at it. Anyway, there was no place for George where his Indian relatives weren't wanted, so he decided not to stake.

Another disputed conversation took place: according to Henderson, he tipped Carmack to the likelihood of a good prospect on the next creek back toward the Yukon, and, again according to Henderson, Carmack agreed to send word back at once if he struck anything worthwhile. Out of this second encounter comes another element, too: it is said the Indians tried to buy tobacco from Henderson but Henderson refused.

The rest takes little telling. The squaw man and his partners struck gold in incredible quantities on Rabbit Creek, renamed Bonanza by a committee of miners a few days later, and they hurried to Forty Mile to stake, spreading word as they went.

The rush took shape at once, emptying every camp and all of Forty Mile. Within days, the whole of the creek was staked.

The man who heard too late to share was one Bob Henderson, still plugging away at the mediocre claim on Gold Bottom.

Seventy years later in the saloons of a dying gold camp on the mud flat where the Klondike spills into the Yukon you can still raise an argument about who wronged whom, about what was said and wasn't said, about the code of the prospector and who was bound by it or what might be just cause for failing its observance.

Whatever the rights and wrongs of that, in 1897 word reached the outside, and in 1898 the passes in the mountains that once had been the sole possession of the Tlingit became the Trail of '98 and thirty thousand fortune seekers poured across to the land of gold.

In 1900 a railway was completed from Skagway on tidewater to Whitehorse on the Yukon and a fleet of paddle-wheelers plied from there to the Klondike.

And the little bands of primitive people, the scattered Athabascan hunters, whose women still preferred to dress a hide with a stone scraper rather than a steel blade, watched in confusion as this voluble horde with its profusion of possessions occupied the river valley at Whitehorse and Dawson City and a score of lesser camps along the way.

They watched and went on with their lives that for millennia had been lived after a pattern drawn from the land and the climate, a pattern in which there was much hardship but much certainty.

Now the pattern was broken and the certainty gone, though the hardship remained.

And maybe those stories, like the ones about Jim Boss that told of a people more picturesque than real, were the whiteman's way of seeing the Indian as vaguely like an odd sort of his own kind, this being the best he could manage, failing to see the reality behind the screen of confusion.

Chapter 5

A couple of hours before the dawn I lit a candle, then started the fire with dry spruce twigs and driftwood we'd brought into the tent in the evening.

Soon we were into the first billy of strong steaming tea. Dave propped on an elbow, sipping at the edges of a hot mugful while I threw together the ingredients of a pancake batter.

Chunks of well-smoked bacon sizzling in the frying pans filled the tent with their hungering smell, and once they were crisp I pushed them to the edges of the pans, then spilled in the batter. The cakes hissed on the hot pans, then bubbled and rose.

I caught Dave's eye in the candlelight. "You hungry?"

He smiled, the question too absurd to answer, then sipped again at his tea. But he answered well when a few minutes later he sat swallowing chunks of bacon and pancake, all awash in maple syrup, chasing the mixture down with gulps from his mug.

When we had eaten every last bit we could, I mixed two large bannocks, setting one in each pan to cook. These would be lunch, wherever we might stop on the riverbank to have them. While they cooked I washed the dishes, then repacked the outfit into the canvas bags used for stowage in the canoe.

As we rolled our bedding the first breaks of dawn were on us, the eastern sky coming light, the trees gathering detail out of the vagueness of their shapes in the receding darkness, the wisps of mist on the still water of the lake showing farther and farther into the distance.

We carried our gear in unhurried trips to the beach by the canoe, stopping each time to search the growing shoreline with eyes all prone to make the shape of a moose at the least suggestion.

Then we struck the tent and stowed the load and put out in the canoe, spreading a wide V of ripples astern on the stillness of the lake.

This stillness promised perhaps another day of the lingering warmth of summer. A dense white mist lay where it had accumulated at the mouth of an incoming stream, and on a far mountain to the west the sun cast its first rosy glance on our stretch of the Territory.

But no wind and no current meant slow going, hard work. It was almost noon before we made out the shape of the end of the lake, well after before we swung about in the quickening current where the river begins again, to go ashore and tie up at Lower Laberge.

Here, where we tied up, lay the wreck of the *Casca,* her ribs rising skeletonlike out of the gravel that the river had dumped amidst her ruins at higher water.

There had been no glory in her dying. She had been dismantled and tied up here in 1911, bargelike, and used as a landing until the river came through her hull.

We lit our tea fire about amidships and tore into the cold bannock. It had been a long paddle since breakfast and the sun had fulfilled its promise of a warm September day.

"No more hard work now, Dave. Current carries us all the way to Dawson."

Dave made room for words past the hunk of bannock on which he chewed. "Easy to go downriver, hard to go up. Long time ago, we got no motors for boat, we got to pole upriver, maybe pull with line where we can walk on bank."

We didn't have a motor either of course, but we had the Whitehorse-Dawson road, which was just as good. An empty freight truck would haul our canoe and outfit, meat and all, back from Dawson City for less than the fuel would cost to power our way back upstream.

Dave munched a little more then added: "What we do sometimes, we make raft, big raft, use good dry log. Then we drift to Dawson, kill moose on the way 'n dry the meat. We get to Dawson, we sell raft for firewood 'n we ride back upriver on steamboat.

You gotta be sure you get to Dawson before last boat. Dawson a hell of a place for Indian to spend the winter."

"Be a nice rest," I suggested, "to ride back up on the steamer."

"Nice on steamer all right. But only three, four days to Little Salmon. I stay Little Salmon most times them days. Best was going downriver on raft. Take plenty of time, stop three, four days, maybe a week to dry meat."

I could see where a month could go by, say you killed three moose and spent the best part of a week camped at each kill, drifting in between.

"One time two boys come over from Fort McPherson, they come on old trail by Blackstone River. They sell their fur in Dawson in springtime and it's pretty late for going back. They have lots fur, they kill lots good marten up toward Porcupine country and maybe Mackenzie side, so they got plenty money. They buy ticket on steamer and all summer they ride up and down, Dawson to Whitehorse. They pay fella in Dawson to care for them dogs and winter comes they go back to Fort McPherson."

I said that sounded like a fine way to spend a summer.

"Yeh," Dave said thoughtfully, "they have good time. It's all new for them boys. They never see big boat before. They never seen train till they get to Whitehorse. They never been to Fort Selkirk and see people up and down Yukon River, so it was big summer for them boys." Then after a pause: "They talk to Indian wherever the boat tie up. I was Carmacks that time I talk to them boys." And of course they would have talked in their limited English, their Athabascan dialects being too far apart. But they were Indian together and that was bigger than language, now the whiteman was in the country.

I dumped the last of the tea, rinsing the billy in the stream.

"Was there much here at Lower Laberge?" I could see a couple of decaying cabins in the brush and an old rusty stove on the bank below.

"Just roadhouse. Steamboat stop here before going on down Thirty Mile. Lots of small boats going downriver, too. People like to stop someplace some nights. Some wood cut here, too."

There had been wood cutting everywhere there was wood to cut.

The big steamers burned a cord an hour coming against the current, and over the years millions of cords were taken from the flat lands of the river bottom and even the hillsides. The steamers stopped on the way to load from the piles on the banks to the cleared decks by the steam boilers.

"You cut wood for the boats much in those days, Dave?"

"Once in a while. Pretty hard work. When fur is good, better to trap. All summer, dry fish for dogs. Winter, keep goin' on trapline, you do all right. Boys make pretty big money cut wood but spend it quick, too."

Perhaps those were the golden years, as the old-timers insist, in their cranky dissatisfaction with the present. Once the first frenzy was over, the life of the Territory settled into a pattern molded by the seasons and the dependence on the river for transport.

Dawson City and Whitehorse were the main settlements and all along the river between a host of camps and landing places, trade points and police posts, wood cutters' cabins and trappers' shacks, Indian villages and mission churches, grew by the way.

Perhaps the Indians who say that they, too, had a good life in riverboat days are not just reacting to the agonies of the present.

They had always lived along the rivers, and a man who had once fished, hunted and trapped could now fish, hunt, trap, cut firewood or work on a boat if he felt like it. There were more places to trade fur, and the White Pass contractor bought whatever wood you had, leaving it to you when or how much you cut.

A man still chose how he lived because he understood the ways there were to live. Only in Dawson City or Whitehorse was there enough liquor to get a man in trouble, and to the people who stayed along the rivers, liquor, used infrequently, was no threat.

It was the construction of the highways and the beaching of the boats that dealt the blow. Everyone left the rivers then and only the places where the highways crossed or came by survived, like Carmacks and Mayo, and these became highway towns like all the rest, turning their backs on the rivers that had once sustained them.

And into shack settlements on the fringes of the highway towns came the Indian people, into a life they did not understand, where the old skills of the river and the forest were of no use, where the responses of a primitive people to a raw environment secured no sustenance, where alcohol offered comfort amid confusion.

The sound of Dave kicking the coals of the tea fire into the river brought me out of these thoughts. We gathered up, then quickly put out in the stream.

The fast current of the Thirty Mile soon took hold of the craft, speeding us along effortlessly, much faster than the river above Laberge.

The Thirty Mile is a narrow stream, with the current shifting suddenly from bank to bank. It runs fast on average, very fast in places. There are no dangerous rapids; indeed there are few dangerous rapids anywhere in the Yukon system, but there are many places where bad judgment will put you over shallow hard riffles, damaging your canoe.

Many lost their lives and more their outfits when the flotilla of '98 passed here.

This motley lot of craft, sawn and hewn and hammered together at the headwaters by the men who'd packed their outfits through the passes in winter to wait for the water to open to carry them down to the gold fields, had already been fortunate beyond belief.

They'd come through Lake Bennett spared of wind.

They'd crossed the mouth of Windy Arm, a gusting choppy fetch of lake that angers under the wind like a northern sea, in a rare moment of calm.

The long reach of Tagish, which could have swamped them all in half a southeast blow, let them pass.

Whitehorse Rapids drowned a number, but having done so, it impressed upon the rest the necessity of going around, and it was short enough to go around.

Lake Laberge supported a light southerly breeze for the passage of those thousands of craft all weighted down with fortune hunters and their outfits.

But the Thirty Mile drew her defiance not from the wind but from the speed of her descent and the boulders on her bed, the

31

thrust of her current across her tortuous channel, the sharp bends of her curves.

She was thirty miles long from the outlet at Laberge to the wide confluence of the Hootalinqua, and there was no going around her.

Upwards of seven thousand craft in that incredible flotilla—boats and barges, cockleshells and rafts, as unlikely as the dream that had brought them here—came headlong down this waterway.

When the stoutly built, the properly loaded and handled, and the plain fortunate emerged in relief on the wide gentle stream at the confluence, the Thirty Mile River was lined with wrecks.

But for us it was a relief after the hard work of Laberge on a warm, windless day to be swept along by these bright green waters, now resting while the current carried us, now paddling furiously to miss a combing roller where unseen rocks lay under.

It was still early when Dave signaled to go in to the east bank of the river just beyond a rapids; but there we camped. It would be too late by the next good ground, and life is not made easy by struggling with hard camps on rough slopes or in alder jungles, camps you are forced into by running out of daylight.

Once the tent was up, Dave led the way to a small stream a hundred yards from camp where there ought to be grayling, he thought.

He lounged on the bank while I tied a fly to a generous length of leader, then cast into the riffles of the stream mouth where the velocity of the water broke on entering the river.

The fly bobbed a moment in the riffles. Then a fin slashed the surface, the line tightened, the rod bent and in a moment the fish, a foot in size, broke the water, before plunging away into the depths of the main stream. Pretending not to be excited but anxious not to lose him, I drew him in, flopping him on the bank beside Dave.

"Whiteman good fisherman," I declared.

"Indian shows him where is fish," Dave replied, taking the grayling to the water's edge, skillfully slitting the underbelly, spilling out the guts.

And I wondered, do I make too much of this joking about whiteman and Indian? Is it really a measure, as I like to think, of

32

our acceptance of our difference that we make these little jokes, or would you really rather I didn't? I cannot ask, for in your endless inoffensiveness you would never tell me. How little we know each other and, little knowing, hide our care.

On the water again my fly raised a strike, then another fish swept it off into the depths. The high dorsal fin rose again to slash the surface, and I brought him in; then one more.

Then nothing further.

"Two fish for me and one for you, you're going to be pretty hungry, Dave." These were large grayling, but a meal of grayling for a hungry man on the river means two on the plate, preferably three.

Dave rose slowly to his feet. Grayling were only as important as they might easily be caught. "We put these by camp. There's little backwater up above. We try there."

So we tried the other place and, perfectly, the river gave us three more fish. Dave cleaned these and we ambled back to camp.

We made our first tea of the camp. Then with a large knife I made fillets from the fish, taking each side off the backbone, then slipping the skin from the flesh. The fillets of white flesh piled on a plate looked neat and accomplished. In the morning I would roll them in cornmeal, then fry them in bacon grease with plenty of pepper.

For the evening meal, I foraged about the grub bags for some onions to put life into tinned beef stew. There's no avoiding it, you fall back on these canned products on the trail, just as others have since '98. Dave, of course, would have traveled with dried meat and fish, tea and sugar and a piece of fish net that he'd set across a stream mouth overnight to keep up his supplies.

Afterwards, we settled in for the long quiet evening in the tent, drinking too much tea, talking a little, sometimes just listening to the river and the sounds of the night.

The smoke from our fire hung in the still air of the river valley in a long layer of haze. Stepping out of the tent before going to bed I could smell it, the dry willow and aspen smoke, making a light fragrance in the night air.

Chapter 6

The next day by noon we reached Hootalinqua, where the Thirty Mile joins the larger river. From here on the silt content is so great you hear the tiny particles rustling against the skin of the canoe.

The Thirty Mile had been narrow and clear, but now in the wide silting valley of the Yukon proper the islands build and erode, shallow bars appear and disappear, and the stream ribbons between obstructions built from its own deposits. Further down, as the volume grows, you may lose the mainstream in places where side channels, promising passage, run out over riffles and trap you against the bars.

In the early days of river traffic Hootalinqua had been an important way point for the White Pass steamers. A boat might winter there for an early run to Dawson City in the spring, and vessels damaged in the Thirty Mile could be repaired.

There had been a stopping house and workshop, a few small cabins and a warehouse. As we paddled by we saw the debris of deserted habitation all about: weathered boards loosened by the wind, a door ajar, a window broken, a stove pipe rusted through.

But on the island in the west side of the channel lay the most remarkable relic of river days of all. Here on the ways, beside the giant capstans that had been used to pull her up, the hulk of the steamer *Evelyn* lay rotting, a hundred miles off in the wilderness from anywhere.

Abandoned long ago, unfit for repair after a mishap on the river, she had sat here through the years as all the traffic of the river passed her by, the spruce and aspen of the island growing up about her, hiding her from view.

34

We tied up alongside and climbed aboard to stand amidst the ruins. Rotting holes gaped in her decks, and in corners here and there the squirrels had stored their cones against the winter.

A heap of heavy coiled manilla lay strewn on the forward main deck, and behind it the boilers, their firedoors ajar and the bricks half crumbled away, stood cold and lifeless, unstoked these many years.

Up the rotting companionway one still could crawl to the cabin deck where the passengers of means had strolled about the lounge and occupied the staterooms, little chambers fitted with bunks and corner basins.

But there was no way of going beyond the cabin deck to the wheelhouse where once command of the steamer had been held. Rot had honeycombed the way and only the sagging shape of the bridge remained.

I looked to Dave in wordless enquiry wondering what he thought of this incongruous hulk. Sensing it, he formed a few slow words: "He's long time here. He's pretty rotten." But I still wondered what he thought, except that I'm sure he sensed as I did the sadness in a dead ship, even here in the unlikely bush of a northern territory where it is hard to believe now that a ship ever had cause to be; and we crawled down as though we had intruded on the poverty of a grand and aging lady, who, having lost her fortune, hides from the world, anxious not to be recognized.

Back in the stream again we slipped along smoothly and we easily reached Big Salmon, a deserted Indian village, to camp that night. Here the Big Salmon River, draining the country to the northeast, joins the Yukon.

The people left the village after the flu epidemic at the end of the First World War, and Dave offered nothing unique about Big Salmon: the people lived here once, but not any more. Well, you could say as much about four hundred miles or more of a river which once had been a ribbon of life and occupation: the people lived here once, but not any more.

But not any more. We choose to live in a certain way at a certain place, we are eager about it and invest the labors of our minds and hands, we build dwellings and supply them, we do all the simple and the complex functions of our existence there, then, quite simply, in response to some external change wrought by forces other than those which we ourselves exert, not any more.

So amidst the deserted cabins of Big Salmon, where the people do not live any more, we made our camp, a good camp, too, though the evening seemed strangely silent and we were early into bed.

The next morning, I woke again before daybreak, lighting the candle. But before I rolled out to fire the stove, Dave spoke up.

"We have short run today. We go only to Little Salmon. We goin' to stay Little Salmon two, three days. I show you my old home. Don't have to cook in the dark this morning."

Well now, damn me if that wasn't pretty nice and made me feel good. Most Indians wouldn't stop a whiteman doing something even if it was as pointless as packing drinking water in January. Old Dave actually intervened for my convenience, and to top it off he'd made a decision about this trip all on his own.

If you don't know the people you might not understand that. They are the most easy-going people in the world. They'll say yes when they really think no, just to get along.

I'd asked Dave to go downriver with me and told him it was his trip as much as mine.

"Look, Dave, we'll just drift down the river, stop here, stop there, kill some moose. You know where there's good moose hunting, that's where we'll stop. You want to do anything else on the way, you say so. Maybe you want to look at some of the old places."

Well, that was all fine with Dave, anything I said. Would he like to go in my canoe? Or would he prefer a river skiff and motor? I knew where I could borrow a skiff and motor.

"Oh, that's fine."

"Which, Dave, the canoe or the boat and motor?"

"Whatever you like."

"Well, I kind of like the canoe, but I'd take the other just as soon. Which would you prefer?"

"Oh, canoe, he's okay."

That's the way it would go, trying to have Dave make a decision or assert himself in some way. And yet here was a man who'd been making useful decisions all his life. He'd never have survived otherwise.

At a time when many of his people are caught in the web of the whiteman's towns, their lives and their children's lives wasting in confusion and drink, old Dave stays by his camp on the road to Carmacks with his wife, living out his life the way he began, rustling for grub, hunting and trapping, busy a little all the time, but never quite busting himself.

Of course, he has an exceptional woman in his wife. He kills a moose, she tans the hide, making moccasins and mitts to sell besides what they need for themselves. He comes home tired with a catch of squirrels to skin, she pitches in and has them half done by the time he's had his tea and boiled moose meat.

Best of all, she doesn't complain if Dave ups and leaves for two or three weeks on a trip somewhere, on the rivers or in the mountains, because she knows that's part of him and he has to do it.

Maybe two or three times a year he'll go to Whitehorse on a little booze-up, and she'll come after him in a few days if he doesn't come home on his own. Nothing unpleasant about it, she just reminds him he's better than all those other guys and it's time to go home, and he goes.

So that's how it was with Dave, and I now had the feeling, which I guess I'd been looking for, that Dave figured I mattered enough to make a decision for me.

I blew out the candle and pushed back down in my sleeping bag. "Sounds fine to me, Dave. I'd sure like that."

Chapter 7

We fell back to sleep and slept ourselves out. It was easily mid-morning by the time we'd cooked, eaten, rolled the outfit and put out on the stream again.

The weather had changed. A high overcast cut away the sun and the air was cool. It was one of those fall days that tells you summer is gone and winter lies ahead, but the moose are fat, the ducks are in the air, the grouse are showing up along the willow swales, and life is on your side.

Noon came and we ignored it. I rustled some bitter chocolate from the stowage, threw half of it forward to Dave, bunched mine into my mouth, then returned to the steady stroke of the paddle. I used my thirst for tea to add to the anticipation of reaching Little Salmon.

Then, unexpectedly, the remnants of the Indian village and the island that lies out from it were suddenly ahead, and we were paddling hard across the current to make the north bank in time not to have to pole our way back up. The mouth of the Little Salmon River opened to our view and closed again, the village drew nearer, the trail up the bank took shape, then, the paddles thrusting a few more times, Dave took us skillfully into a fragment of a backwater that held the canoe while he stepped ashore with the bow line.

"Good shot, Dave." I tossed my paddle beside the mound of gear forward, waiting for Dave to tie fast to an aspen tree, then pull the canoe over by the gunwale to lie by the bank. I brought a stern line out as I stepped ashore and we made that fast as well.

"Where do we camp?"

"Top of trail. All level ground so we camp close to canoe. But we just make tea now and walk around. After, we make camp."

I scurried for the billy and the grub bag and scrambled up the bank. Dave already had some wood and soon the wait for lunch was over. Then we went for Dave's walk.

Little stood of what once had been one of the major Indian villages of the upper Yukon. At one time two or three dozen good cabins, an Anglican church, a trading post and an assortment of caches had lined the bank. Now there stood only the shell of the church and a few fallen cabins.

The rest had caved in long since under the weight of their own sod roofs. They lay now in diminishing heaps that barely marked the pattern of the site where all the serious urgencies of life had once been carried on.

We stopped before the outlines of the foundations of a long disappeared cabin. Dave looked at the ground in front of him, then up and down the long line of ruins, some no more certain than this.

"Here is where my Daddy has cabin. I'm small boy here, before we go to Carmacks, long time ago."

"But you lived here when you were grown up, too, didn't you?"

"Yeh. I live with my wife's people when I first married. They have house over there." He indicated an upstream direction. "Then I have my own cabin, but I stay Carmacks, too, sometimes Yukon Crossing."

We walked on a few dozen yards, coming to the end of the village clearing. Then we followed a path through a young growth of aspens, soon reaching a burial ground where more recent structures than any of the cabins stood in abundance. Over every grave stood a grave house, about four feet high, structurally a typical whiteman's rectangular house with pitched roof and glass windows, traditionally a borrowed custom from the coastal Tlingit who traded here so long ago.

There were thirty or more, many recently painted. Considering the decay of the village, this surprised me and I asked about it.

"Some people die Carmacks, we bury him Little Salmon. Not any more, but some old people, after everyone leave here, they have to come back when they die. 'N sometimes, some people come up to fix grave. But not any more, I guess. People don't care much for grave any more."

Care might be waning now; once it had been abundant. For all those here, some treasured object, useful in the time after death, lay in offering.

Through the windows of the grave houses, one saw the tin plate and cup, here and there a sewing awl, in one a new aluminum pot bought especially for the leaving, Taylor and Drury's price tag yet in place; in a smaller house over a child's grave, a toy truck and a bright toy pistol.

We read the names on headboards and granite stones. These also were in the trade line of Taylor and Drury, ordered out by mail, brought in over the White Pass Railway and down the river by steamer.

But these were all the graves of people of the river-traffic days, of the years of Taylor and Drury at Little Salmon and the resident Anglican missionary.

"This must be an old camp before the whiteman, Dave. The people would have been here to catch the salmon in the river mouth." Perhaps they built weirs in the channels of the Little Salmon, catching the concentrating spawning runs more readily than in the wide sweep of the Yukon.

"There is another old graveyard, I show you maybe tomorrow. Old, old place. I don't know how old. Long time ago, too, I don't know if Indian uses graveyard. I think he burns dead body, buries just ashes, some special place."

Dave turned down the trail then, back to the village site and the canoe. "Best we make camp now. Weather maybe turns bad."

We made a good camp; when you know you'll be in a camp long enough, you want the best. We cut small thick-branched spruce trees back in the woods then dragged them out, limbing them off to make a thick mattress of brush all over the floor of the tent. We put the coarser boughs at the doorway to walk on so the sand and dirt from our boots would fall through to the ground; the finer, softer ones we laid with the bend upward for a springy mattress beneath our bedding.

We set the tent with care then banked the hem with earth to seal the joint of tent to ground against the cold fall air.

In the tent we fussed with the level of the stove and laid out our gear just so. Finally, we strung light rope from pole to pole above our heads for a place to hang a towel and clothing to dry.

Then we lit the stove and the heat drew out the fragrance of the spruce boughs, filling the tent.

"Pretty snug, huh, Dave?"

"She's damn fine camp."

With an hour or two of daylight left I managed, with effort, to think of leaving the warmth of the tent, even the billy of tea it would have been so pleasant to brew.

"Let's shoot some grouse." I had a single-shot 20-gauge in the canoe and we were in the rise of the grouse cycle. Any willow draw ought to give up a bird or two. "You bring your 30-30 in case we stumble on a moose, and I'll show you how to get a feed of chicken."

"First, I show you where is chicken."

So we gathered up our warm wool jackets and our guns, and indeed it wasn't long before the sudden beat of willow grouse wings startled us on the trail. We'd set out on a path leading away toward the flat timbered land of the river confluence to search along the beaver dams of a tributary creek, but before we reached the draw of that watercourse we flushed eight or ten birds.

I shot three out of that covey and we went on. Twenty minutes later we came on half a dozen spruce hens, killing five of them.

This was too easy. We sat on a log with eight grouse on the ground before us, deciding they were all we could use.

I turned the talk to moose. "You think we should try to kill a bull here? We could get somebody at Carmacks to take the meat up the road to your wife, and we could keep on going down the river for some more."

"Moose here, but he's long way back from the river. We got to pack him too far. We get one close, we take him. Maybe we get one close, too. Lotsa moose, anywhere you get a little lucky, you find him."

I realized I had been worrying over the possibility of killing a moose before we reached Carmacks and upsetting the trip as I had planned it.

When you take the river route from Whitehorse to Dawson

City, you cross the highway just once, at Carmacks, the former river settlement named after George Carmack of discovery claim on Bonanza, who had a cabin nearby before the events of August in 1896.

And so, hunting down from Whitehorse, you can come off the river at Carmacks if you kill before you reach there. If not, you go on and you could come off again another day's run down at Minto Landing where the road and river brush by each other for the last time before the Klondike itself.

These are welcome options, too, for the man whose main concern is meat, particularly if the mid-September weather is warmer than average and seven or eight hundred pounds of prime bull would be better off in a deep freeze than lying about in a canoe for another week.

But while I fully intended to make a kill on this trip, the purpose of the trip was more to enjoy a leisurely run of the whole of the river to the Klondike, with as many days and as many camps as that could reasonably entail, all in the company of old Dave.

Kill one moose up river of Carmacks—we could send the meat to Dave's wife on the road south of Carmacks. Kill two, and we'd have to think about coming off the river. Kill three, on the basis that Dave as an Indian trapper was entitled to all he could use, and there'd be no question of going on.

Kill one moose below Carmacks and send it up to his wife, maybe one or two more before Minto Landing, what then?

What I had in mind was not to look very hard for moose at all until we were among the islands below Fort Selkirk. Then we might camp a few days in one likely place after another until, with all assurance, we'd have a full load of meat.

I worried about these plans of mine and how they might be upset: on the one hand really pleased with Dave for assuming direction of our affairs and holding us here at Little Salmon, on the other apprehensive that while poking around here we might find compelling use for our rifles, upsetting the hopes I had for the rest of the journey.

But I couldn't explain all that to the placid bronze face sitting on the log beside me, sharing an hour and a day so sufficient already in its short run of river, its good camp well made, its yield of willow grouse and spruce hens, its promise of good holding weather for meat in the new coolness of the air, and its anticipation of hot tea and grub and a long untroubled evening in the candlelight of the tent.

I doubted that Dave ever planned ahead except in general terms of securing a supply of grub against tomorrow's needs: of taking fish from the river in the summer, killing meat in the fall, trapping the upland fur in the early winter, ice fishing a little at the same time, then hunting the beaver in the spring in an almost festive ritual of the returning sun.

I could land in Dave's camp any day, any time of year, to propose a trip of any reasonable sort for the following week, and Dave would return my enthusiasm with the usual, "Sure, he's fine by me."

I'd repeat myself in three or four ingenious restatements of my proposal just to be certain Dave understood, because damned if you could be sure from any of his typical replies whether he was clear what day, how we'd travel, how long we'd be gone.

But everything would be fine with him and give or take a day or two for something that might have cropped up in the meantime—such as the fact that his brother-in-law had wanted him to help pack in some meat, or that his credit at the trader's had grown too high and he'd had to cut a few cords of wood—he'd be there, all ready to go.

Might be a somewhat hand-to-mouth way to live, but within the limits there was a lot of freedom in it.

Dave broke into my thoughts. "I think he's might rain tonight. We go back now, we cut a little wood before dark."

So we gathered up the grouse and then turned down the trail toward the river and the old village again.

And it did rain, but in the warmth of the tent and the soft glow of the candlelight we could listen to it, wind-driven against the canvas, with particular pleasure.

Chapter 8

The rain let up again in the morning and we walked back into the timber, spending an hour finding our way through a swamp created by beavers damming a stream. The swamp, Dave explained, hadn't been there in the old days. Too many hunters, no chance for beaver when the village was occupied.

Then we came to the older cemetery, but Dave couldn't tell much about it. Here the very old people were buried, people who'd been old when Dave was very young, Indian men and women who had lived the greater part of their lives knowing little of whitemen, seeing only so much of their goods as came through the coastal mountains with the hard-bargaining Tlingit.

Perhaps the people before that were buried here, too, but Dave wasn't sure at all for he knew from his grandfather that there had been a time when the people did not bury their dead in this way.

We climbed a high hill to the northwest, looking down over many miles of the Yukon valley and up the broad draw of the Little Salmon. Northward lay the valley of Frenchman Lake and a trail that comes out on the highway now above Carmacks. You could go that way long ago to Yukon Crossing on the winter trail to the Klondike, too.

We sat together on a fallen log and Dave scanned country in which he had lived the greater part of his life. Indeed, in the whole of it he had not ventured farther from here than a man might travel by dog team, raft or river steamer.

How many salmon had he dried, how many moose killed, how many rabbits snared, how many lynx, fox, squirrel, marten, wolverine and beaver taken from these hills and mountains and rivers to pay the eternal credit at the trader's, credit for what had crept into the Indian life as necessities: tea, sugar, rice, flour, beans, fish net, firearms, ammunition, traps, rope, canvas, axes, swede saws, nails, knives, rubber boots, wool socks, wool underwear, wool blankets, duffle cloth for parkas, needles and thread, beads, heavy stoves for cabins, light sheet stoves for camping, stove pipe, cooking pots, frying pans, lard in pails so the pails would become tea billies, candles, lanterns and kerosene for the lanterns, and matches—above all, perhaps, matches.

I wondered if Dave pondered these things as I did for him in his company, but I knew not nor ever would, except that on this day and the days that followed Dave grew alternately more silent than usual, then unexpectedly fluent, telling a story, persistently, invariably of long ago, of what had happened to his people here in these converging valleys of the Yukon and the Little Salmon.

After a long while Dave rose, to begin walking along the ridge at the break of the slope where the timber gave way to the grass, his carbine loosely held and swinging lightly, his pace easy, his eyes habitually searching the timber at the foot of the ridge. A few paces behind, I followed, my heavier rifle hanging by the sling over my shoulder, muzzle down, the scope protected by the bend of my arm.

The wind picked up. Heavy gray clouds scudded across the northern sky, high above the hills. Aspen trees, smitten yellow by earlier frosts, gave up their leaves in sudden flurries.

Eventually, Dave turned down the slope into the timber of the bottomland. Soon we came to a stream where we lit a fire and lunched on what we'd stowed on a packboard on leaving camp.

Dave had taken the packboard in the morning, so I picked it up after we put out the fire, cradling my rifle in front on a crooked arm because you can't hang both a rifle and a packboard strap on your shoulder at the same time.

We followed old trails through tall, mature spruce, often passing the signs of a long ago camp: a few poles left where a tent had been set, a black pot still hanging in a tree where it had been left for use on another planned journey that had never been made, the ashes of a fire cold for many years.

Once in the heart of a swamp we came on an old meat rack. It had been hastily put up where a moose had been killed, used once for the drying of the meat, and would remain there until even the dry air of the Yukon would rot it away.

We saw much sign of moose, and I wondered what Dave's intentions were. A long way from camp, we were too far to pack meat unless we dried it.

Still we penetrated the timbered valley and Dave's attention seemed little taken by the fresh-punched moose tracks in the moss or the heaps of recent dung.

At last we came on a cabin by a small stream, an old and tiny cabin of the sort a trapper sets on his line for overnight shelter. No more than ten by fourteen feet, one narrow door, a peep-hole-sized window, and a sod roof completed it. And it was old as everything is old that has been left to the forest and the winter snows.

We pushed open the door, entering slowly in curious awe. Inside stood the remnants of a stove and a bunk of split poles. On the floor lay the fragments of earlier use: a candle stub, an empty tin, a chipped enamel cup. On the wall there stuck a calendar of thirty years ago, into a gap between the logs a newspaper of fifty.

"Somebody's old trap cabin?" My voice intruded on the trance of yesteryear.

"Some boys trap this way from Carmacks, they used to use this cabin. But long time back, he's built by whiteman. He gets old here all by himself and gets crazy. Police take him away."

It is an old story. A man came here in search of fortune perhaps, of escape more likely. A rare few found fortune. For others, the loneliness of trapping in a remote valley for their small living intensified until reality slipped away.

We pulled the door closed on leaving, and now Dave turned back directly, walking quickly on a well-defined trail, as though for a reason all his own he'd made a pilgrimage of sorts and was free to return to the more regular business of the river, the camp and the pursuit of moose.

We came out of the timber just at dark, tired and ever so grateful that our ready-made camp waited for us.

The next day we ignored time once more with the delicious

impudence of the man who has freed himself of all commitment and has at hand, for the interval, all he wants or cares for.

We'd eaten our grouse, so we shot some more. Then we went out in another wide-ranging ramble north of the river, climbing a great deal and resting for long intervals at choice look-out spots.

The day after that, we nearly threw all our leisure away.

We were on a low ridge skirting a wide swamp, perhaps five miles from camp. We'd been wandering about, looking at old camp sites, following the network of trails that earlier occupation of these valleys had imprinted upon them, pushing open the creaking doors of three more ancient cabins, foraging around in the back yard of Dave's nostalgia.

The ridge afforded an excellent search of the swamp. We moved slowly in hunting fashion, so it really wasn't surprising, having stopped motionless for some minutes to search the sounds below us, that we caught the snap of a twig hit by an antler, then the rattling of the great spreading palms thrashing impatiently against a willow bush.

The rut was only a few days off, and the caution of the bulls even now receded. Soon the crash of antler on antler in deadly earnest would replace this first flexing of neck muscles against light brush and saplings.

Picking up a dry stick Dave went to an alder bush thirty feet away, then slashed up and down the bush with the stick. The dry wood clunking against the green stems of the alder made a dull drumming, like the sound reaching us out of the swamp.

Dave stopped and we searched the wind intently with our ears, but idly, too, for neither of us had quite had time to lose the mood of our wandering.

Then we heard him coming, on the dead run, and our whole awareness narrowed down to the focus of the hunter confronted by his quarry.

I dropped to the ground, propping myself on my elbows as I roughly aligned the scope in the direction of the crashing brush.

Dave knelt beside his alder bush, his carbine half raised.

For a fraction of a moment I wished we'd talked about this, confirming some understanding. Dave had spoken about not killing

47

a moose too far away for handy packing, but I was unsure what he might be thinking now and there was no way to ask. When the bull appeared, the first man with a good shot had to use it or pass it up, all on his own.

Then the bull appeared. My safety slid off. The bull stopped, head up, half in belligerence, half in alarm.

He stood immense, the Alaskan bull moose in his full and splendid growth.

I forgot the debate about whether to kill or not, falling into the responses built over many seasons of searching and shooting for the meat on my table.

My eye dropped behind the scope and the crosshairs settled on his neck just back of the ears.

"Hoo ah!"

I jerked my head up.

Dave had jumped to his feet and flung his stick in the direction of the bull. The bull bolted from sight and Dave turned to grin in my direction.

"We shoot that bull," he declared, "we have to stay here all winter to eat him up. Down river, we kill lots close to canoe."

Well, I was relieved, both because I'd been saved a hell of a job of meat packing in laborious packboard loads and because Dave shared my notion about spoiling the trip if we killed before we reached the lazy channels and backwaters of the lower river. Or maybe it was his notion, and I shared it.

I gathered myself up and we struck out for camp, traveling fast, making plenty of noise. We weren't taking any more of those chances.

And so it went for the first four days and nights at Little Salmon: lazy breakfasts taken in daylight, long easy forays into the valleys or high up the ridge tops, with leisurely stops for boiling tea and munching bannock by the river or a side stream, stops in which the talk came easily to Dave while I disciplined myself to listen.

Then in the late of the afternoon, when the cool of the air turned distinctly sharp, we'd return, walk weary but not exhausted, to stoke the stove and fry the breasts of willow grouse, then settle into a long, easy evening in the warmth of the tent, the air touched with wood smoke and spruce boughs, the candle throwing shifting shadows on the canvas of the teepee.

We'd lie on our bedding, moving occasionally for comfort, sometimes reaching over to put fresh water in the billy, coats rolled beneath our heads for pillows, listening to the gusting wind and the periodic surge of current in the passing river.

Dave's storytelling grew in confidence, and as it did so I began to realize that all the piecemeal yarning of these past few days really told one long story, a story of such importance that in its telling I think he forgot that I was there, if not the presence of us both.

It was in the last evening that he tied it all together, and the hours of our own night were quite forgotten.

Chapter 9

It was before the people had guns and before the large dogs for pulling toboggans had been brought into the country.

Life was difficult. But later, when everyone had dogs and could haul much meat and a whole camp outfit from place to place, they sometimes complained they spent more time hunting and fishing to feed the dogs than themselves.

So perhaps when all this happened, life seemed no harder or easier for the people than now. They lived how they understood to live. Life was changing because of the trade with the Tlingit, but no one even imagined the big changes yet to come.

K'Anta was born in that time, somewhere on the Yukon well below the lake now called Laberge but well above the mouth of the Pelly. It may have been by Little Salmon, but no one can be certain.

His father was a good hunter, careful in everything he did. His mother matched his father's skill with tireless industry in all her work. Between them they always had what they needed, even in the hardest times in the very late winter when food ran short and the melting snow made travel impossible.

When his father had still been a young man, he'd had a dream, alone in the mountains, hunting the caribou in late summer. He saw the caribou shedding their antlers all in one place, in a great pile. He didn't know the meaning of his dream at the time, but he sought the spirit of the caribou people as his helper in his hunting, and he stayed in the mountains alone for many days until the frost came hard and the high ridges began to be covered in snow.

During this time he killed no caribou although he had many chances. He was wise, for the caribou people came again in his dreams and always they shed their antlers in one place, making a huge pile before him in his dream.

Finally, when he came down from the mountain to return to his people, he came on caribou only a day's walk from the camp, killing twice before the herd went too far for him to follow. But he was able to come back with his brothers to set many snares and have much meat for winter for all their families.

And the meaning of the dream was this: that the caribou spirit would be his helper and the pile of antlers represented the antlers of the many caribou he would kill in his lifetime.

He took care never to offend the caribou and whenever he killed, which he did so often it brought notice among the people, he spoke with respect.

"Forgive me what I have done here," he would say. "I am only a poor hunter in need of meat for my family, and I will take care not to let the wolves at your bones." Then he would be as good as his word, careful not to offend.

It was fortunate for K'Anta that he was the son of a careful and provident hunter.

He was fortunate in his mother as well.

For all the hides that came in the camp, she never wasted a bit of one worth working. Only the early summer hide of the caribou, riddled with warble larvae holes, would be let go and these she disposed of so they wouldn't be ragged about by wolves in insult to the caribou people.

With her supply of hides continuously in some part of the tanning process, she also sewed ahead for the family's clothing, teaching K'Anta's sisters how to do the work at the same time. If one of the men accidentally soaked his moccasins he didn't have to wait for another pair to be made. She had spare pairs to be worn while the others were dried slowly, worked by one of the girls every little while to keep them from hardening as the moisture left the leather.

She cooked carefully, saving every scrap of food, wasting nothing.

She kept an orderly camp, changing the brush often to keep the sleeping places clean and warm.

And she always had snares out for small game: rabbits in the fall and winter and gophers during the short summer season.

In those days, several families camped together. This was mainly for the hunting, so three or four men could work together, driving animals into the pounds or hazing them toward a snaring fence.

And if one man's luck ran down, then the others could help him out. Once when K'Anta's uncle had suffered a whole winter in which he killed nothing because his wife had handled his snare rope when she was menstruating, K'Anta's father and his oldest son supplied him with meat.

But nothing so stupid could happen to K'Anta's father's hunting luck, for nowhere among the people was there a woman more careful of herself than K'Anta's mother. She left the main camp at the first warning, staying in the menstrual hut some distance off for the whole time each month. She would take some unimportant sewing that would be for her own use during that time: never anything that might later be used by her husband while hunting. The evil power of the menstrual condition could not be avoided, but only a foolish and lazy woman would take chances with it.

As K'Anta grew old enough to notice, he realized his father had much respect from the other men. He decided the important questions: when to hunt, whether to drive into a pound or use arrows, when to move the camp into a different place to winter.

The others left him the first choice of meat at the large fire where all the families cooked together.

At the times of the year when other camps came together with his own, at beaver trapping and at the trading ground, he spoke for his camp, which included his own family, his wife's brother's family, an older son and his wife with their first child, and an older woman, cousin to K'Anta's mother, who was a second but less favored wife to K'Anta's uncle.

K'Anta learned this also about his mother: that while she never directly told the other women what to do, she did largely run the camp, dividing the work among them all, instructing the girl children herself, and tactfully keeping her sister-in-law from bringing endless bad luck on the camp through her lazy ways about her time each month.

She had the responsibility when a girl child came of age in the camp of supervising her seclusion out of the main camp into a puberty hut. When K'Anta's older cousin had been in the hut, he'd mischievously tried to get her to break the taboo and look at him and her brother of his own age. She had refused, ignoring their taunts. She had been too well prepared. But when K'Anta's mother heard of it, K'Anta and his cousin had a lesson in the dangers of contempt for the power latent in the world of his people which would last them a lifetime.

Lessons did not have to be taught twice to K'Anta, and one lesson going on all the time in the confining atmosphere of many in-laws in one camp was in the relationships between the men and their women.

He saw from his uncle there was little one could do with a lazy and careless woman but beat her when one had to, and bear her the rest of the time. One didn't interfere with this, either. Once, when her cries as he punished her were most piteous and everyone in the camp but his uncle knew that on this occasion she wasn't at fault, K'Anta saw his father turn away without expression when his mother, wordlessly, looked imploringly toward him.

Still, he saw his uncle favored her over his other wife. He puzzled on this until his own developing maturity taught him the difference between an aging woman and one still young and sexual. This realization brought another: that a man did not marry only for a mate to share the tasks of survival, to tan hides and sew while he pressed the search for game, but also so that the powerful urge within him to sow his seed could be fulfilled.

It was his uncle's misery that he had married for this, failing until too late to see the laziness of the woman who attracted him so forcefully. Little wonder his disappointment so often turned to anger. Then when he married the older woman, hoping to find in her the competence the other lacked, he found he had erred again, for though she worked skillfully he now had sexual obligations to a woman he found unattractive, even repulsive. On top of that he wasn't a good enough hunter to support two wives. He had only complicated his life, solving nothing. He grew more angry with his first wife, believing her responsible.

There were times because of his uncle's marriage relationships that the camp was not happy. But the vital work went on because his mother saw that it did. When her sister-in-law grew truculent or sulked after being struck, she somehow started her doing something useful, even though much of the time she would have to do all the harder, more tiresome parts for her. The woman rarely saw a hide through from start to finish. But she would sew, and her sewing was useful even though no one could take pride in it. K'Anta often saw his mother give her a beautifully soft piece of her own tanning to get the other woman busy again.

Between his parents K'Anta saw how different marriage could be.

They spoke quietly, his mother with her eyes down, his father looking a little off to the side. One saw no emotion, never any anger. The words were of the work that must be done, how long the meat and fish might last, when the camp would have to move and, when moving, where the women would stop to make the camp while the men went on ahead to hunt.

He never spoke to her about the training of the girl children, nor she to him about the boys.

Once, when they lost a child, a little girl who had lived just so long as to learn to laugh and win their hearts, she grieved so deeply she fell away from her work, neglecting the camp even after the ashes of the child had been cold for many days.

Without her, the other women began to quarrel. The camp fell into disarray and a half-tanned hide dried hard as wood on the stretching frame.

K'Anta's father grieved deeply, too, as indeed they all did, but food ran low and still he could not go out to hunt unless his wife could bring herself to her work again.

Finally he went to where she sat on the bank of the river, her head on her knees, her arms folded around her face. K'Anta was with her then, trying to offer comfort. But the little sister had won his heart, too, and only by a desperate will did he stop himself from running into the bush to hide tears of his own.

54

K'Anta moved aside when his father came to kneel by his mother. For a long while he did not speak, waiting for her to realize he was there.

Then: "You have to come back to us. You have to stop your grieving now."

There was no answer. It was as though she hadn't heard, and indeed the words were said half-heartedly, as if words of any sort were meaningless in the face of so much grief.

Then he drew her arms apart, forcefully lifting her face, but gently at the same time. For a long time they looked at each other.

"How can I stop? I wish that I too might die and be with my child."

"You do not know what you say!" he cried, with an urgency K'Anta had never heard before. "She has not long been gone and she might easily gather you! You must not say it! You must watch out against it."

Again they did not speak for some moments.

When he spoke again, it was in the familiar terms of need. "The meat is little in the cache. Maybe only one day, two days more. I have to go to hunt and I must take all the men, for we dare not fail. Your sister-in-law is quarrelsome and our son's wife has lost her sense for some reason. She thinks because we are all mixed up with our loss, she doesn't have to do her work. And there is a good hide going to waste for want of a woman to tend it."

For a while longer, in this highly exceptional way, they looked directly into each other's face, and seeing it K'Anta drew away, ashamed that he had intruded on a frightening intimacy.

His mother went to the river then to splash water over the stains of her tears, and when she came back in the camp she was herself. Within the hour the men had gone to hunt and the women to their work.

In all the years of K'Anta's boyhood, his father did not find it necessary to strike her and K'Anta realized, in time, he never had.

K'Anta could recall only once when it might easily have happened, when most men would have delivered punishment of some sort.

It had been during cold weather. One of the girls had begun her first time in the evening and said nothing, perhaps not being fully aware.

But the outcry among the women in the morning when they had discovered that the child must have lain in the camp the whole night in her condition, told everyone at once what had happened.

The men were to hunt that very day and their weapons had all been nearby.

It was disastrous. There is nothing so evil as the condition of a girl child at her first time. It is for her mother to be sure by her cautions that the child goes out of the camp at once. To lie through a whole night in the main camp with men who must be successful in the hunt if the people are to eat is to fail in the worst possible way.

K'Anta's mother hadn't been the one to discover it, but she knew from the cries of the others what had happened. Quickly she had thrown warm clothing at the child, ordering her out of the camp at the same time. Then she had gathered some burning sticks from the fire and followed her, taking her to the hut, making her her own small fire.

When she had come back she had had much to gather for the child, and then she had to think of every small observance by which she might reduce the danger to the camp.

But first she had walked directly to her husband and stood before him, submitting but without visible fear.

The camp had fallen silent. Others who had been doing some small chores, stopped and turned away. K'Anta, knowing the significance of what had happened, had turned away his face but not his eyes. He stood but a few feet off.

His father's face had been shaken as he had rarely seen it. For a long time he looked at his wife.

Then he had spoken. "Do whatever you can that will help." And he had walked away.

Chapter 10

For his first years his people let him amuse himself: but long before he left his mother's side, his games with his cousin turned on what they overheard of hunting from the men.

In a more real pursuit he followed his mother as she tended her snares, running ahead to be first to see which had caught a rabbit, careful all the while not to disturb the rabbit trail over which the snare was set.

Disappointed that only some of the snares would have rabbits each morning, he urged his mother to set more snares to make up for the empty ones. She pretended to complain that already her son expected nothing but more and more work of a woman. But she seemed in some way pleased to have this complaint to make and she did set more snares, to K'Anta's huge delight.

Before long this wouldn't do, either: he asked for some thongs for himself, pretending he needed them for a game with his cousin.

She gave him some short pieces of little use and at once he was off down the snare trail to several places he had already chosen, where a little fallen brush forced the rabbits to converge their trails.

Just as he had seen his mother, he made the sets. By tying the bits of thong together he had enough for three rather scrappy-looking snares. For a long while then he stood at a distance, watching his sets, hoping to see the rabbits come and be caught. Fortunately for his hunting success, he grew cold and had to return to camp.

The next morning he had great difficulty waiting for his mother to go around the snares, then as much difficulty pretending it was really a matter of indifference whether they went around the snares or not.

He went in front as usual, but walked instead of running. Still, he made sure to be well ahead by the time he reached his own snares and as he had rather begun to fear, there was no rabbit in any of them. And no fresh tracks showed in the light dusting of snow in the trails leading to them.

He wondered if he should change them in some way but wasn't sure how, and in any case he didn't care to do anything with them in front of his mother who by now was catching up. So he went along to the next of her snares as though there was nothing unusual about the existence of his own sets or the fact that on this particular morning, they didn't happen to have caught any rabbits.

He hoped his mother might not even notice and indeed she seemed not to have. On the other hand, when they returned to camp she handed him, without a word, a dozen pieces of thong, every one a good long piece fit for a set without any skimping.

This time, K'Anta spent the rest of the morning making his sets, looking more closely at the places his mother had chosen for hers, studying the trails in the snow, seeing which were still used and which had not been trampled for many nights.

The next morning a rabbit hung from his third set, just as they did from his mother's, frozen in the limp position of death.

He waited for his mother to catch up so she would be sure to see, then played the game of indifference more deliberately than ever. He cleared the snare then tossed the carcass to his mother, just as he did when he helped her with her own catch. But now, conscious of his mother watching, he remade the set himself.

They went on and in two more of his snares there were rabbits.

His life as a hunter had begun by his mother's side in pursuit of women's game. But no weakness lay in this. A few snares travel with every hunter, and by setting them as he makes his bivouac at night he keeps himself in food along the trail.

No notice was made. K'Anta was not even sure if his mother told his father. He knew that when he killed his first significant game there would be feasting and his father would make gifts to the people of K'Anta's own moiety, the Crow. But this was in the future and no attention would be paid in the meantime to rabbits caught by the camp, useful as these might be.

Still, even if it was less than noteworthy that he had caught rabbits before his voice deepened, his father told pointedly how a boy in his uncle's cousin's family had been such a poor hunter from the start that he had not even caught rabbits before he left his mother's side.

From the first, K'Anta's parents had prepared him to be a hunter.

At his babyhood they had hung a beaver hand on his cradle so he might share the wisdom of Beaver Man, the wisest person who had ever lived.

When he was still small his father had put him on a wolverine pelt on the snow. "Let him be as the wolverine, not to feel the cold," he had said, leaving the child a long while to be sure the magic of the pelt would work.

When he had begun to eat meat, his mother had given him a little of the tissue from the inside of the hide of a wolf to chew so he would have the speed and endurance of that animal in the hunt. So that he did not later lose this, they had warned him against carrying stones about; they had particularly instructed him not to put them in his clothing pockets.

As he lost his first teeth they taught him to rub each one on a stone then leave it in a rotten stump in the forest where it would never be found and to find a different stump for each tooth. His new teeth would be sharp then and would last him all his life.

Well before his voice changed his father took him from his mother's side to begin his training in earnest.

K'Anta learned new ways to set a snare, special ways for each animal. He was given thongs so he might practice braiding many strands together while he watched the men making the rawhide ropes, thick and strong, to set for sheep and caribou and, most powerful of all, the great bull moose.

He learned the artful deadfall, where to set and how to bait it: most important this, now that the smaller animals were killed for their fur, especially the marten, for the trade with the Tlingit. Already the camp had two cooking pots, two of the men had steel knives and K'Anta's father had a steel axe head.

These tools made the work of a hunter easier, especially the knives. Skinning and butchering took only part of the time it had with the stone blades. Although these cost much fur, the people were grateful for them. Now they hoped, if they could catch enough fur, the Tlingit might bring the guns of which they had heard from others farther up the river.

So while K'Anta learned about the deadfall, he heard also much talk of the Tlingit traders, of the price of knives and of the unbelievable guns that could kill moose from a great distance and so easily the people might never again go short of food.

K'Anta longed for his first true hunting bow, thick-staved and strong, fit to drive the hardened antler arrowhead through the hide of the largest moose.

For while the people depended for their main food on their skill in setting snares, each man still prized most the game he killed with his bow by patiently stalking an animal until, from closest range, the arrow could be driven with certainty through the tough hide.

One of the pleasures of a well-supplied camp was that a man could leave the more organized hunting for a time, going out to prove again to himself and his people that he had yet that consummate skill to track and stalk and kill alone in the forest or on the mountain slopes, matched against the elusiveness of the quarry and the exhaustion of the trail.

No sweeter moment existed than when he would walk quietly into camp, all bits of blood carefully cleaned from his person, his pack load of meat left by the trail a short way back.

All eyes would be on him, seeking the answer to the question no one would ask, but he would pretend not to notice.

He would put down his little traveling sack, then hang his bow and the arrow bag in a tree a little way off from the shelter.

He would sigh and stretch, remarking how tired he was for it is a long way to the mountain, then come in by the fire for the food his wife would offer him.

60

He would eat of the dried meat. Then, looking on it with deliberation and hoping by now that the whole camp believed him to be as empty-handed as he tried to pretend, he would make an off-hand comment.

"It would be good to have a little fresh meat for a change from this we dried so long ago. If someone has nothing better to do, they might go up the trail and fetch my pack. I almost got it here, but I had packed it so far, I thought some one might not mind bringing it the rest of the way."

The camp would not fail him. The children would run about telling the news over and over again, the boys making the motions of creeping along the ground, then drawing back the bow.

The women would fuss a little for his extra comfort, and his wife would tell his sister, who had pretended not to hear because of their avoidance relationship.

When the meat arrived in camp it would be prepared and eaten in a festive way, and all through the evening as they ate of it before the fire, he would tell and retell the story, encouraged by the generous questions of the other men.

K'Anta had seen this many times, and the measure of his destiny as a hunter was that he longed in his heart to come casually into the camp himself, in exactly such a way.

Little wonder that he felt impatient for his first true bow, rather than the play bows and arrows his father had given him, the usefulness of which he had long since exhausted.

But a bow is of no use to a man who does not know the ways of the animals, and this his father kept him to learning over the seasons after he left his mother's side, until several seasons after the season his voice changed.

He traveled constantly in that time with his father, the two of them alone or in the company of the other men. He helped to build the long brush fence in the way of the natural escape of the sheep from a mountain slope where at certain times they could be sure to be found. Gaps narrow enough to let only one animal through were left in the fence and set with a snare.

Later he followed his father as the men, having seen the sheep on the slope from afar, crept into wide-ranging positions from which, in every direction, they frightened the animals against the fence.

For the first time he realized how swift of foot was his father.

When the sheep had first taken fright they had bolted in one direction then another, blocked each time by a hunter who jumped from cover before them.

Then as they ran toward the concealed fence the men pursued them, to be there behind them should they shy back away from the strange obstruction. In panic then the sheep would bolt for the narrow openings and if the men were truly fast of foot, they might ensure a sheep in every snare.

K'Anta had run and raced at play with the other children in the camp. The fastest among them, he ran sometimes just for the joy of feeling the wind against his chest.

But he was unprepared for what happened now. As the pursuit across the slope began, his father suddenly sped away, hardly looking down at the uneven ground over which he ran.

K'Anta, running with the ease and zest he always had, and slowed only slightly by the steepness of the slope and the stones under foot, expected to catch up with him, thinking only that his father had started a little sooner. But it did not happen, and in a rush of anxiety K'Anta sprinted with all his strength.

His father disappeared over the slope where the sheep had run, and gasping for breath, he reached the crest himself only to find his father even farther in the distance, up to the sheep now, joined by the other men, all shouting and waving their arms at the milling, terrified animals.

K'Anta stumbled along the slope puffing heavily. Finally, he had to go on at no more than a jog until he'd caught up with the others.

The sheep were in the snares, thrashing in their death struggles. K'Anta arrived exhausted, heaving for breath and staggered by the commotion before him. A large ram threw himself upward, twisted in mid-air as the noose jerked his neck, flipped over, then came down on the rocks on his back so sharply K'Anta heard the bones break. A death cry, wild and agonizing, cut the air.

K'Anta's father rushed in on the ram, opening the throat with

62

his knife. The blood, pumped by the last beat of the heart, spilled out, bright crimson, on the brown and yellow moss of the mountain slope.

Then he looked for his son, and K'Anta, bewildered by the speed with which it all had happened, met his eyes.

"Here. Loosen the snare and untie it from the fence. Coil it carefully. It will kill for us again some day."

And K'Anta went forward then, relieved that his father did not seem to have noticed his failure and anxious to be of use.

His father went to help the others and K'Anta, his breath caught now, put a finger in the fresh blood then passed it to his tongue.

"It will be better next time," he said to himself, aloud.

After that, whenever he had cause or just free time to do it in, he ran. As long and hard as he could, he ran. Until his lungs seemed about to burst for want of air and his legs begged him to stop, he ran. Then he ran on even farther, when all that kept him going was an iron will and the memory of the day on the mountain slope when his father left him standing still.

His legs developed into powerful springlike cords of sinewy muscle, separately visible beneath the skin, and his lungs grew to suck the air.

K'Anta learned when the fish came to the river and how to build the traps; when the pike were in the shallows of the lakes and how to set the nets; when the caribou were high in the mountains and when they could be found in the timbered valleys; when the moose rutted and could be called into range of the bow; indeed, how the weather and the life habits in every season told when and how each animal or fish might be taken so that the camp could be defended from hunger, and the people could live.

And while he learned from his father his uncle sought him out in free moments in the camp, for there was much to learn besides hunting.

He learned that he had been born a Crow and that from the beginning people had been divided into the Crow and the Wolf so each could help the other.

In time of death, each moiety handled the other's dead.

And wherever you went among even the farthest camps of the people you would find your moiety, Crow or Wolf, and you were certain of the help you might need.

Most important, Crow married Wolf and Wolf married Crow, and this rule was never broken. K'Anta was Crow like his mother and his uncle on her side, but his father was Wolf. And when he married, he must marry Wolf. His children would be Wolf like their mother, and so K'Anta's seed would give his father grandchildren in his own moiety.

These things and many more of the complicated kinship system of the people were taught him by his uncle, although it was difficult to sort out those that had been explained from those that he had absorbed simply because they had functioned around him since birth.

Already he knew he must avoid his sisters, not speaking directly to them. But his uncle clarified that he might joke with a prospective mother-in-law before he married, yet avoid direct talk with her afterward, even while for the rest of his life he would have strong obligations to help her to live.

In such ways the months and years of his learning went on. The days of his play forgotten, he grew wise in the ways by which the small hunting group took enough meat to keep the camp in so harsh a land.

Chapter 11

As he grew K'Anta became more aware of the cyclic way the camp went about the year's activities.

After the long winter the camps of the people gathered. They hunted beaver for the greasy flesh, much craved after the lean meat and dried fish of the late winter diet, and for the pelts, not to be traded but used in clothing and robes.

Many camps would gather in this almost festive time. The people would sit about the fires in the evenings while the old men recounted the stories of the past, and friends would tell each other of the hardships of their winter, of the passing of their old ones, of infants born into the camps.

A time of lake fishing followed while the rivers ran high in the early summer flood and the game animals, taken only if convenient, had yet to build the layers of fat which made them choice in the late summer and fall.

The groups that had gathered for beaver hunting stayed together for the fishing in some cases and dispersed in others, depending on fishing rights, kinship and the size of the different lakes.

Then before the camps dispersed again to the fishing sites along the main river and its tributaries they all gathered at the trade place to wait for the Tlingit who already would be packing in along the trails, seeking the people for their furs.

If the Tlingit came, they would trade at this place. Otherwise they must disperse along the river anyway and the Tlingit must follow them there, for once the salmon arrived no camp dared fail to catch and dry every possible fish. If bad hunting fell on any camp, fish and rabbits would be their only hope; and when the rabbits failed, as every few years they did, then the dried fish might be the only means of survival.

In either case, each man had with him the furs he hoped to trade. When the Tlingit arrived, trading partners sought each other and bargained for several days. The custom of trading in partnerships, a Tlingit for each man among the people, had been in use for many seasons. The partners came to know each other, making the trading more certain.

Young men, trading the first time, had to establish partnerships, feeling their way into the customs of bargaining.

Trading time was tense. The people appreciated the goods the Tlingit brought, but still they felt strongly the great effort it had cost them to catch the fur. They felt they should get more for the fur. Particularly they wanted the Tlingit to bring guns, with the powder and bullets they had heard about and which indeed they suspected the Tlingit had with them even then, secreted back along the trail.

The Tlingit replied that they packed the trade goods a long way from the coast: surely the people must realize the Tlingit really got very little for all their effort . . .

With the trading over, the fishing on the river continued as long as there were fish to catch and dry.

But when the runs played out, the people moved into the fall and winter camps to kill the now fat moose, caribou and sheep, to enjoy a time of plenty while shoring up against the long winter.

During the last of the fishing and the first of the hunting, the women picked berries, drying and packing them down in bark containers.

So in all these essential activities of the passing seasons it was in the late spring and early summer that the people gathered for a while into larger groups than the extended family units of the winter camps. Songs were sung, stories told, feasts given and marriages arranged.

This time was important to the young for without it they had only the stories of the elders in their own camps to offer them a notion of the world of the people and their place in it.

In his earliest years K'Anta had rushed about among the shelters with the other children, so many it seemed he would never straighten them all out in his mind. But straighten them he did and through them the kinships of his small society.

He had found which cooking pots he might reach into as if they were his own, which he mightn't. He had discovered who avoided whom—and whom he had to avoid.

He had found another uncle who favored him and a grandmother who sang him songs, strange chanting songs of a lost husband whose spirit wandered beyond the mountains, never returning.

Now that he was older, he grew more reserved with the other boys and avoided the girls, with many of whom he had a strict avoidance relationship anyway, through kinship. His associations were fewer, but through them he still added to his knowledge of the people.

He found the old grandmother to be nearly everybody's grandmother, one way or the other, and her song was for a husband she had lost when she had been young. He had died in a storm in the mountains and been eaten by wolves before the people could find him to cremate the body. His soul would wander forever, unable to return in reincarnation in a new infant as the souls of the dead do if nothing goes wrong. She did not sing to K'Anta anymore but always to the little ones, one of whom could have been the lost hunter if only the wolves had not eaten the body.

He found the old hunter with a torn ear never spoke with the man whose wife had the patch of pale skin on her face. They had once camped together and the half-eared one had tried to use a kinship advantage to share the other's wife. Afterwards each accused the other of using magic against him, and the half-eared one accused the woman of witchcraft, saying the pale skin on her face was where the evil powers had entered her body even before she was born.

He found some who were known by all the people to dislike each other even more than these two but who remained polite, visiting each other, even exchanging gifts of food.

It was a season for relationships to change.

A son-in-law might take his wife from her parents' camp for

the first time, to begin living in his parents' camp. She would have a while to get used to it, still able to visit her parents before the camps broke up.

Another man, seeing his wife's parents growing unable to manage might ask them to join his camp. Or he might give up his present association with other relatives to go back with the old couple, perhaps encouraging another related hunter to join him to make up a more workable group.

An older man or woman, losing a spouse in the winter, would quietly take another, for in the hardships of the hunting life the team is fundamental. If necessary, among the older people, two women would share a man or two men one woman, the necessity of the work relationship overcoming the jealousy that might occur among younger people attempting the same solution.

Only one old man remained single. By the time K'Anta had grown to realize his uniqueness he also knew the story that accounted for his peculiar seasonal antic.

They called him One Without Teeth. He had broken all the top teeth at the front of his mouth in a fall on a rock slope when he was young. His startlingly ugly appearance, along with an awkward limp from the same accident, had made him an unfortunate but utterly ridiculous oddity of just the sort little boys cannot help imitating and with such persistence that their parents, failing to conceal their amusement, cannot stop them.

K'Anta had been guilty in his turn until his father caught him at it, and it was the one enduring stroke of shame out of his childhood that stayed with him, searing him inwardly whenever he thought of it.

One Without Teeth had an average skill in the hunt but his uncertainty about his personal worth, reinforced by his parents' doubts, had prevented him from seeking a wife. He had, therefore, never done bride service or imposed on his parents the task, a dubious one in his case, of offering a marriage gift.

He had lived with his parents until they died, his mother doing the work for him a wife would have done, tanning the hides and making his clothes.

Then he had moved to the camp of a younger brother who

had been happy to have him. He was thought to bring good luck, and his brother had good ground in which to use an extra hunter. Neither did his brother's wife object though she now had to sew clothes for an extra man in the camp.

The joke started one beaver-hunting time. The women began to tease him, saying he should really get busy and find a wife, something they would have thought preposterous if anyone had suggested it seriously.

They gathered together some hides and a few furs they cajoled from their husbands and brothers-in-law, making up a semblance of a marriage gift. This they pushed into his arms, urging him to take it quickly and offer it to a woman in the next shelter whose daughter was marriageable but hadn't been sought.

Seeing the joke and delighted they had gone to the trouble, he did as they urged, horrifying the woman with his offering, saying he had to make the gift himself since he had no parents to do it for him.

The laughter from the others gave it all away at once, but the joke had been so good it must be repeated, and before long One Without Teeth had made his offer to every mother of a marriageable girl in the camp, followed by more and more laughter on the part of the women for it was, without doubt, a woman's joke.

Then the next season it had been such a good joke, it had to be played again. But of course now the mothers approached with the gift knew the joke, too, so they played their part, feigning astonishment.

It became One Without Teeth's own joke after that. When the women tired of it he took his own marriage gift, of the furs he had caught in the winter and would later trade to the Tlingit, going the rounds of the shelters. People hadn't the heart to stop him so they went along with it, often without enthusiasm.

And so he now went on, old age compounding the absurdity, and people weren't sure he didn't believe himself to be on a perfectly serious mission. It became pathetic to see him, the limp more pronounced, the aging face suffering more and more the injury of long ago.

But what had become a bizarre pursuit with One Without Teeth remained a vital matter for the young.

Even while the year's marriages were arranged and fulfilled, the even younger men, hoping to be hunters enough to seek a wife in a season or two, would have the chance to think of this girl or that.

Some watched closely for industry: others, smitten by a half-turned face and a supple figure, found themselves in a strange new agony, wondering how they would survive till they might have their parents' permission.

But for K'Anta there was no speculating about a future wife. His preoccupations were yet with his own unfinished tasks. He watched events, he listened to the elders, he studied the trading, noticing who among his own people knew a little of the coastal tongue, who among the Tlingit could speak a few of the words of the people, in a strange and foreign way. All this he watched sensing that he had too much yet to learn, that his manhood was too far off, that he must waste no moments until he had the skills of the hunter, knew the kinships of the people, possessed his own furs to trade, understood the bargaining and could walk among his people as a man, recognized as K'Anta.

Chapter 12

K'Anta's father understood the boy's impatience, but he would not put aside in his son's making the caution that had fostered success in his own life.

K'Anta was not his first son, but in K'Anta he saw the hope of every father for the son who would excel beyond him. He did not know why it was this boy any more than the other two, but it was this boy, and as surely as he had cherished the hope so had the boy begun to fulfill it: from the intentness of his hunting games through the snaring of his first rabbits to the deliberate conditioning of his body for the hunt, he had begun to fulfill the hope of the father.

Little wonder then that the hunting bow was not fashioned until in all caution the boy could be sure to be ready. For this boy must not have the bow and carry it a winter, perhaps two winters, yet fail to kill big game. This boy must not, being tried too soon, lose confidence and then, anxious and unsure, lacking the bold certainty of success, expect to fail. It would be all too easy after that to fulfill, instead of the hope of the father, the expectation of failure.

Still, neither must wait too long, the father to give the bow nor the boy to become a man, since neither could bear the unspoken questions that would follow on too long waiting. Why does he not make the boy a bow? Is he afraid the boy won't know what to do with it? But you see he prides himself how quickly the boy learns his work. Ah, but perhaps he is not so sure after all. Really, there is nothing so special about this boy, K'Anta.

His father grew relentless, imposing a spartan strictness on his son and himself together.

He slept across the fire from his wife all the time now, not only for the days preceding a hunt.

His equipment—his bow and arrows, the detachable heads, the knife—all hung in a tree far apart from the camp. If they wanted tending in any way, he left the fire to tend them. He did not so much as bring a knife into the shelter where he might lounge as he sharpened it.

Together they ate sparingly and only of the meat of the great animals of the forest and the mountain, the moose and caribou and sheep.

And K'Anta, conscious of the determination of his father, formed his own commitment not to fail. In the camp, where they spent less and less of their time now, he kept to himself, avoiding his siblings and cousins, courteously but firmly reducing even his notice of his mother.

He slept without a robe, determinedly keeping his body from shivering in the cold as the fire died away in the night.

Increasingly, their time was spent on the trail.

The fish runs had been good and the camp had dried a large supply. Then, in the early days of the fall camp, the men had been led to hunt with an urgency that puzzled them at first. But this was explained when, with a cache full of meat ensured, K'Anta's father abandoned the leadership of the others to hunt only with the boy.

They hunted at first the moose, in wide-ranging forays from camp, along the bottom lands of the river valley and in the timbered hills between the tributaries, staying out each time until they killed.

The rut was full on at this time, and by imitating the grunt of the cow or by rattling the dried shoulder blade of a previous kill against the willow stems in imitation of antlers thrashing, they could entice the bulls into range.

They lay together, the boy and the man, listening for the crash of the approaching beast and when it came, the man would draw back the string of the bow while the boy, his body taut with the excitement of the primeval confrontation, would say to himself,

72

not yet, not yet, until the bull, nostrils steaming and great flanks heaving, came so near the smell of him filled the air.

And when the boy said to himself, *now,* silently inside him, his own fingers releasing an imaginary string, so also did his father send the arrow driving, to penetrate the thick hide and the yielding flesh at the point where the organs of life lie close to the surface.

Then they would track the fleeing animal after allowing him time to weaken, cutting in large half circles around the track until in a while they came on him, dead or waiting to die, unable to rise.

They traveled light on the hunting trails, taking no robe for warmth at night and only a little dried meat to eat. They carried snares, for it was unthinkable to travel without them, but in their avoidance of small food animals they never set them.

Indeed they hardly ate or rested. Like the bull moose in the rut that forsakes all food or rest, they forsook all food save the scraps of dried meat; all comfort save a small fire at night, sleeping hunched before it, coming to it late and leaving early, sparing no daylight from the hunt.

When they killed they returned to the main camp, each packing a load of meat as large as he could carry. They would spend a night in camp then return the following day to the kill with the other men to fetch the remainder of the meat.

Then they would set out again as relentlessly as before, as if by the persistence of his killing the father could make certain of the son's success.

When the bulls became too advanced in the rut to be fit for meat, they turned to the cows. Now they hunted with their ears, straining for every sound in the wilderness, moving slowly through the timber in short, stealthy walks, listening for far longer intervals than they moved.

Then out of all the sounds they would hear the sound of the cow. But she would not come at them like the bull and hunting her was slow and risky.

Coming up wind, they must approach without so much as the snap of a twig.

73

If she hid beyond cover too thick to penetrate, in silence they must wait for her to move.

Above all they had to wait, motionless for hours, until what might be done, might be done in certainty.

The stalk did not always succeed. But when it failed it was not that they alarmed her or became impatient, giving up after long hours of waiting: only that sometimes the opportunity never came and the cow, unaware of their presence, moved away in another direction, traveling beyond their reach.

Then they would begin again, persisting in every hour of light as the days of fall grew shorter.

Then the snow came and because the first fall or two was wet they carried spare moccasins, one pair hung loosely on their packs to dry while they wore the other. But soon the weather sharpened and the snow came cold and dry.

Now her tracks gave away the cow. They would find her trail then pursue her in wide circles, approaching each time from downwind, with utter caution, to find her without themselves being found. Then, as before, they made the final stalk; however much time it took, however cold they became, they waited, motionless in the snow for the chance to move a little closer, and finally to shoot.

Then the bright crimson blood, spattering on the snow, made the final tracking down a certainty.

They ate more now, mostly when they killed, for the cold drew on their strength as much as the distance of the trail and the weight of their packs. Their bodies, shed of all fat, sinewy and lithe, possessed of much endurance, yielded up energy for every demand.

The meat piled high in the caches of the camp. Now would be the time, now that the winter's food was assured, to hunt for fur against another season's trading. But K'Anta's father might have forgotten about furs for all the attention he paid to the season for setting deadfalls. The others began to gather fur between meat packing trips, but still the leading trapper among them pursued his single purpose.

And now the question lived in the camp, though no one would ever ask it. When? How long would this go on before the man saw fit to leave the boy to find the truth alone? When? Surely it was time.

It was asked in the eyes of the men who sensed that too much was made of it, that the boy, so driven, had no room to back out, to take his time, to feel his way alone a little perhaps, to come on his chance more easily.

It was asked in the eyes of the women who worried for the man and the boy, especially the mother who watched the lean body of her son, so strong but still so young, wondering how long the strength could grow without ebbing when used so hard.

But the boy did not ask it. His attention fastened only on the hunt, on the pursuit and killing of game, in such bond with the father that they thought and acted as one.

The two passed their days almost without words.

They rose from their hunched positions before the fire together, then made their simple meal.

They set out on the trail together, seeking the spoor of the moose.

Together they reached down to test the tracks with their fingers, in one accord judging the animal, how old the sign, how fast the pace, whether to begin the wide downwind circling at once or to follow a while dead in the tracks.

To move, to lie still, to listen, to move again: never any words, a glance perhaps, often not even that.

The two were as one, and together they had moved farther back into the primeval land than even the hunting camps of their people. They hunted as the wolf hunts: constantly, without respite, in utter, single purpose, to kill and so to survive.

The hand of the boy was one with the hand of the father, and the hand of the father held the string on the bow, the taut string singing with the power of the bending wood poised behind the shaft and the deadly sharpened arrowhead.

So with the meat piled high in the cache the father and the son left again after only two nights since their last kill, to go to the mountain for caribou.

It was early to hunt caribou. The restless beasts, their long-ranging legs rarely still, would yet be on the mountain slopes, ignoring the gathering cold, eating the moss on the ridge tops where the tireless wind never lets the snow settle to cover the ground.

When winter deepened they would come into the timbered valleys where the yellow moss lies beneath the trees, where the snow does not pack under the impact of the wind and their wide round hoofs may paw it aside to expose the feed.

Later yet they would forage for food in the lowest valleys and might be surrounded for easy killing as they strung in long lines of travel across the ice of the larger lakes or rested in thickets of spruce on the wind-swept winter shores.

The man and the boy left in the dark of morning. The mountains where the caribou ranged lay two days walk in ordinary circumstances. They camped, well after night had fallen on the day of their departure, at the foot of the mountain in sight of the slopes.

The cold air of winter, severe and penetrating, forced them to tend their fire through the night, yet still they slept hunched by the blaze on a mat of boughs, waking at intervals to put on the wood they'd gathered at hand.

At daybreak they walked out at once from the thickets to search the open ground above them.

For a long time there was nothing, and when K'Anta saw the caribou he wondered if his father already knew they were there, but was waiting for him to see them for himself.

He could not at first be sure. Several times his eyes had come back to a distant cluster of black spots, waited for them to move, then ranged on again in the search across the slopes, waiting for other clusters to move or confirm their existence as rock or brush, outcropping through the snow.

Then the one group moved, not in the sudden flight inspired by wolves but in the stop and start of the feeding travel, now slowly, now quickly, now stopped, now moving on.

K'Anta looked to his father to find the older man waiting for him to do so. His father then dropped to one knee, removed a

76

mitt and, holding his fingers in a loose group, punched them several times in the snow, making a cluster of holes.

Then he drew a line from the cluster of holes in the direction of movement of the caribou.

Next, he put two finger holes down to show where they themselves now stood and a long line from there to a point of intersection with the other line.

Here, in this situation, at this time, you do not pursue, not even in wide downwind circles. You intercept.

They started up the slope, boldly and quickly with much ground to cover, and the distance alone gave them hiding. All the while they watched the caribou herd, following its movement, gauging its changes, gauging its speed.

As the distance narrowed they sought cover, traveling in low ground, avoiding the crests between depressions, however slight, for against the sky the movement might be seen.

Then they closed no more distance. Instead, they stayed with a draw that led all the way up the slope and into a saddle that must lead into the next valley. They stayed in this for cover and to reach a level at least a little higher than the caribou before they would search them out again.

The sun, low now in its winter path, had moved far along the hills over which it rolled by the time they stopped their climb to seek the best way out of the draw to locate the animals once more.

They chose a thicket of the willowy bush that grows to a man's hip on the mountain slopes, in patches here and there. They crawled out to this cover then rose to search the ground in their view, little by little, to see without being seen.

The caribou had moved upward, but still they moved toward the draw.

The men dropped back, retreating into the draw, then began their upward climb once more.

When next they crept to the edge of cover the caribou had dispersed over the slope and their direction of travel was impossible to predict.

The hunters moved further up the slope, then out to the edge of the draw once more. They now lay within a short climb of the saddle and ridge crest itself. The sun was near the end of its travel.

The caribou had moved into a compact herd, heading up the slope toward the saddle, into the wind.

Quickly the men moved up the rest of the slope.

The wind, favorable all day, now became a factor. They dare not go so far ahead that a shift of wind would carry their scent. Yet they must go far ahead if they were to intercept at all. They hurried on, nearly running but sure of foot, their moccasins silent in the shallow powdery snow.

At the crest, in the saddle itself, they came once more to the edge of cover. They crept across the ground on their stomachs toward the expected path of the caribou, but they stopped when they had risked the wind all they dared.

The herd came toward them, traveling fast, feeding little. K'Anta feared their scent would reach the closest animals.

Then the caribou, in one of their sudden shifts of direction, unaccountable but taken on the instant by the entire herd, moved off the predicted path, away from the hunters, then upward again to cross the ridge top many times an arrow's flight from the saddle where the men lay in wait.

There was no light for another attempt. The hunters went directly to a long tongue of timber that snaked up the mountain slope in a protected draw, so they might camp and begin again in the morning without a climb.

Once more they bivouacked in their spartan fashion, though the cold crept into K'Anta's limbs, making sleep hard. But he ate sparingly of his dry meat both night and morning for the hunter does not know how long he might have to get by on this little food he has spared himself from his family, while he hunts far from camp that they might not face hunger in the long nights of winter.

They found the caribou the next day before the sun had reached half its path. They had been wise to camp high on the mountain for now the caribou lay still, as they rarely do, and the hunters were above them. The animals were in a draw below, one or two moving about, the others in their beds. The clear day and the weakening sun had made an invitation to rest.

78

The caribou had stopped to rest. Not so the hunters.

They crept down the slope, first making sure of the wind. They had good cover, which would bring them to the resting caribou on the far side from the sentinel animals.

They were out of sight as they worked down but they had memorized the draw and every clump of brush where the caribou lay. They knew the place from which the animals would be in view again and from there they would shoot.

Two cows, young and fat, had just risen to their feet.

These two were in arrow shot.

The hunter laid four arrows just ahead of the clear space where he would draw the bow.

Then he fitted a fifth to the string.

The string drew back, bending the resilient wood, back, back, back.

Now.

Inside him, K'Anta said it. Now. Before it is too late. Now, for now is the time.

The arrow had not spilt the blood of the first animal on the snow before the second arrow was speeding on its way.

The herd bolted and in moments had gone far across the mountain slope, out of sight. By nightfall it would be beyond the mountain, perhaps halfway across the next.

But struggling behind, heavily wounded, two animals weakened. The hunters ran them down, and the last of their life spilled out on the snow.

Each hunter dressed an animal, removing the skin and taking the meat from the bones. Then they laid the skins and the meat out separately on the packed snow so everything would cool.

A long way down the slope below them stood the first timber they would reach on their way. There they would camp and also burn the bones of the caribou so the wolves would not rag them about, causing offence to the caribou people.

Soon they left, wrapping everything in the skins, pulling it all behind them.

Then after they had built a large fire to burn the bones and a separate one to cook a little of the meat for their own meal, they fashioned the hides into makeshift toboggans with the meat packed evenly in the loads, leaving it all to freeze into shape overnight for the journey.

In two days they were home, bringing their meat into camp.

The next day they did not go out.

Instead, K'Anta's father built a small shelter apart from the main camp, a little leanto with a floor of brush, and before it he lit a small fire. He gathered wood enough to last a while, fetching also a pot with some meat to cook in it.

Then he brought from a place on top of the cache, far from the reach of children or women, where he had long ago stored it to season, a fine straight stem of wood, free of knots, true in the grain, thick but supple, such a piece of wood as a hunter might use to make a bow for his son.

For two days he worked on the bow and for two more he fashioned the arrows, with detachable heads of hardened antler. And during this time he slept in his shelter away from the camp, preparing his own food, gathering his own wood. The women kept away, not even glancing toward his leanto and they made the children play on the far side of the camp.

K'Anta avoided everyone, spending much of his time outside the camp.

He knew that the time had come.

Chapter 13

K'Anta knew what the whole camp knew: that indeed his father had left no way but the way of success, to be reached in a short, fast hunt of only a few days' duration, a hunt that must begin and conclude like an arrow on a true path from a powerful bow.

This was not usual. The time of training, of learning the ways of the animals and the vagaries of the seasons, of stiffening against the hardships of the trail, would normally take several seasons at least.

The first bow would be made with precaution, but little notice. The boy would begin to carry it while yet in the company of his father, and if good luck brought the chance, he would shoot his first serious arrow from his father's side.

If he missed, nothing need be said. If for a season or two he did not make a kill, it would pass without comment. There would yet be time. Not all good hunters do well at first.

He would do his share in group hunting: tending snares, driving into the pounds, packing the meat to camp. Then, all in good time, he would make the first kill truly his own.

His father would mark the time with feasting and gift giving, appropriate to how well his son had killed and depending, too, on the season of the year and the provisions in the cache. A man with poor territory or whose own skills in the hunt barely kept his family ahead of starvation might not mark the event at all.

Indeed, few young hunters breaking into manhood would have borne the severity of K'Anta's father's faith in his son, nor the consequent intensity with which he thrust him into the mold.

But there were few young hunters like K'Anta. This was a fact of faith with the father and therefore with the son.

The others sensed it, too, but unspoken remained the one difficult question: how does this boy come back into camp if, for any number of reasons that might befall the most experienced hunter, he does not kill within the few days his little supply of trail food will last? It is winter now, and the severe cold of the dry snow wind may begin at any time.

When the bow was being made, just as the whole camp deliberately ignored the man in his shelter apart, where he scraped the stave to a perfect taper, a perfect balance, so also the whole camp knew every sliver, every shaving, knew every heft by which the balance was measured, knew the time draw nearer and nearer as the bow, then the arrows, one by one, were finished.

So much had been made of it.

When this boy goes out of this camp, he will come back a hunter or he will not come back at all.

When the bow and the arrows were finished, K'Anta's father hung them in a tree near the camp but away from the traveled paths of the women.

Then he returned to the main brush shelter to eat with the rest of the camp. He sat by his son, and the women remained apart from them both.

Still his father went to the separate shelter to sleep, and K'Anta knew that there he would remain until, in a few days, he, K'Anta, could release him from his avoidance.

K'Anta rose early, long before daybreak.

He gathered his small hunting bag with the flint and the tinder, his stone knife and an amulet, a tooth from the jaw of a caribou, a few snares, which he intended not to use, and a sparse supply of dried meat.

Then he ate well of some meat he had himself set to cook by the fire the night before.

He knew where the bow had been left, though nothing had been said of it. He went to the place where his father hung his own bow and took down the new one, and the arrow bag beside it, hardly looking at either as he did so, trying not to acknowledge the strange excitement running through him from the palm which held the fresh-shaped wood.

82

For a moment, he stood before the little shelter where his father lay, covered in his robes. But his father did not stir, though both knew the other was aware. Nor did K'Anta expect it, for each perfectly understood the position of the other and there was no need of acknowledgment.

Then he left, taking alone the trail to the hunting grounds.

His plan had been clear in his mind for some time. He would follow the trail to the caribou mountain to a place not quite half-way there where he and his father had several times found moose and where, on their return with the caribou meat, they had crossed fresh sign.

This would give him a beginning with several choices. He could scout for fresh sign, and if he found it, there were several half-open places along a creek bank where the moose might be exposed as they browsed on the tender willow shoots, the substance of their winter feed.

If this failed, he could cut wide circles to find which way the moose had gone, and if that failed, he could go on to the mountain for caribou.

For a moment he let himself dream idly of coming on a moose unexpectedly close to camp, then killing it and returning, setting the whole camp in an uproar at his tremendous good fortune.

But he banished this wayward daydream as quickly as it had come, fearful of the consequences. He was never sure the spirits of the moose people did not somehow read his thoughts, as surely as they would hear his words if, on killing an animal, he spoke disparagingly of it.

By daybreak, he was out of the wide river valley, into the tributary valley where the main hunting grounds of his father began, in the bottom lands of the several creeks and in the low hill country between them, reaching far to the headwaters and the mountains where the caribou and sheep were found.

The main trail branched and converged, offering choices to the hunter. He might stay in the main valley all the way to the mountains, he might foray up side streams or cut into the hills in several likely places.

83

Generations of hunters before him, searching these same valleys and hills in the same quest for survival, had made their different choices and imprinted on the hunting territory a pattern of trails, used also by the game they sought, which in turn their descendants would use, add to, then pass on to yet later generations.

K'Anta made a choice.

He took a trail that would lead him over several low ridge crests, offering a view down into the creek bottoms where moose, browsing in the early morning, might be given away, their blackness vivid against the shallow snow.

It was now early winter. The snow did not yet demand the use of snowshoes, but in one or two stiff falls it easily could. Neither had the harsh deep cold which follows the shortest days arrived. But it might at any time, and the hunter watched the sky for warning of the wind of the dry cold snow for when it began it would be followed by terrible cold as day is followed by night.

The rut is almost over by this time of year. The bulls, once so fat and prime, are lean and stringy, the meat blue beneath the skin, the strong rank smell of the rut imbedded in the flesh.

Only a hunter pressed for meat and despairing of doing better will kill a bull now, unless it is visibly a young bull, kept out of the breeding by the older bulls and still a little fat.

It is the cow he seeks. Of the cows, he prefers the dry cow—the cow that never calved this season past or, calving, lost her young to wolves or to a grizzly bear.

Nor may the hunter expect to run an animal down as he will in late winter after the snow is deep and crusted, when, with his snowshoes, he will skim along on top like the wolf while the tiring quarry ahead of him will break through at every lunge.

In those circumstances, the exhausted moose lets the hunter come closer each time before taking flight. Then closer becomes too close and the barbed arrowhead, driven through the hide, works inward until some organ vital to life is injured.

Hunting in the deep crusted snow, the hunter has no need to stay hidden, no fear of snapping a twig to incite flight in his quarry, for it is flight he promotes.

84

But now, in the shallow snow of early winter, the hunter must not only carefully choose his moose and forego the convenience of calling it into range, he must also approach so close, without giving his presence away in the wind or by sight, that the arrow, driven against the tough, unyielding hide, may break its way through.

K'Anta stood on the high ground of each low ridge he crossed, scanning all the ground below him, spending as much time watching and listening now as moving.

The silence itself was audible. Out of it, somewhere, would come the sounds of a moose, for even the cow, foraging for willow shoots, does not move in complete silence.

Once he saw a bull browsing. For this animal the rut then was over. But even at a distance the hip bones could be seen through the thick winter hair.

K'Anta passed on, giving no alarm.

Eventually, he took the lower trails again for he had passed the time of day the moose would feed. They would bed down now, in spruce thickets or in alder clumps.

Less-determined hunters make a fire at this time of day, resting while the moose rests, going out again in the late afternoon to hunt through the last of the light into the dusk.

Not so K'Anta.

He began making wide circles in the bottom land, among the willow clumps and through the spruce stands, sometimes in alder, after the track he sought.

Several times he circled, silently, with all caution. While he sought now the track, rather than the animal itself, he had no wish to jump a moose from its bed by accident and, unready with the arrow, to fail in the sudden moment of hunter and quarry being startled together.

Then late in the day he cut across the track he sought—the track of the cow, crossed twice by the track of a bull, but not anywhere followed by the track of a calf.

He knelt by the imprint on the trail, taking his hand from the mitt, softly touching the snow that had tumbled into the track as the foot had withdrawn.

It was firm, refrozen into the shape it had fallen. But the tiny white balls of night snow, which do not come from clouds but fall sometimes out of clear air in earliest morning, were not present in the tracks though they could be seen faintly on the surface surrounding. Neither were there flakes of frost in the track itself.

The track had been made at daybreak or a little after. Somewhere ahead, perhaps only a short walk away, even now she lay resting, sleeping a little but alert to her back trail, no more than a moment away from the flight she would take at the least warning of pursuit.

K'Anta stayed on her track for a short way until he had confirmed what he suspected: she had been by here near daybreak, and after that she had begun to feed, browsing on the clumps of willow, bending down and breaking the bigger stems with her powerful bite to get at the high, tender shoots.

The wind was nearly still. What wind there was drifted down the trail the cow had made and, since he had no further need for a while for what the tracks could tell him, K'Anta went away from them, on the side farthest from the course of the creek that threaded through the willow bottom where somewhere she lay at rest and would remain, if undisturbed.

He moved in a wide curve so that instead of going away from her track he traveled parallel to it, but well away, near the hill.

Then, in response to the judgment of his conditioned instincts, he turned again, back toward where the track would lie if the cow had kept moving. As he neared the expected trail of split hoof prints in the snow, his pace slowed.

Sometimes, several moments passed in the shifting of one moccasined foot.

His ears and his eyes strained in the search.

He did not cross her track again, even when he reached the half-open water of the creek course, but he had not expected to.

He was downwind of her now. Somewhere between here and where he had left her track earlier, somewhere within the large half circle he had himself described in his movements, she lay in her bed.

He would now prefer that she were up and moving about again.

Bedded in the snow, she might remain hidden from sight until he was nearly upon her.

If he waited until she would be certain to be moving, there would be little time left.

If he pressed the search now, he ran the risk of alarming her before he could see her. This called for an arrow already set upon the bow, the bow itself half poised, everything hanging on the skill with which a fast-shot arrow might be sped after a fleeing animal.

He moved to the cover of some half-grown spruce standing at the edge of the willows that grew next to the creek—the same long span of willow clumps in which some distance away he had first found the track.

He gathered green branches, silently, to make a mat on the snow, then knelt down to wait and to listen.

When the sun had only a little way to go he moved out again, traveling slowly up the wind toward her.

A few steps. Search and listen.

Another step. Listen again. Listen hard for every sound in all the forest. Listen.

The day slips by, you cannot stop it. The sun has only one more dent in the hills to go.

Move a little more, away from the creek then back toward it again.

Listen. Listen for the muffled sound of a hoof on a windfall, listen for the snap of a dry twig under the hoof, listen for the breaking of the thick willow branch as she tears it down with her bite.

Yes. Listen, for there you hear it. Unmistakably, there she is. She browses there, do you hear it? Yes.

Now you will move more cautiously than ever in all your life before, for you dare not lose her.

Your hand trembles and your heart thumps wildly in your breast for so much hangs here now and so little would throw it all away.

But nothing will throw it all away so surely as the trembling hand and the thumping heart. But you know that, young hunter. You know that, not because your father told you, because your father told you practically nothing: but because you crept by your father's side until, indeed, your hand was with his hand and your heart was with his heart and all the things your father knows passed into your being while you were so conjoined.

So your hand trembles and your heart thumps, but you know about that and you will not fail, just as your forefathers, hunters before you from the beginning of the world, must not have failed, for you could not be here if they had.

No, you will not fail, but you might not succeed yet, either.

K'Anta made certain where she stood, hidden beyond several clumps of willow.

He saw a way, if he moved a little to one side, that he would reduce the cover between them.

Carefully, he so moved.

Now, if he moved again, his chance to see her might be better yet and, if he did, he would be close enough to shoot.

Again he moved.

But after that he moved no more.

She browsed only beyond the bush she fed on. If she came around into view, he would kill her.

If she moved in the other directions, directions in which she would remain in cover, he would not see her.

But now he must wait. He fitted an arrow against the shaft and half drew the string. Having done everything else the hunter must do, now he must wait, and this, the waiting, is the most important of all.

With his ears and his eyes straining, he followed her movements. He could hear the rustling of the willow brush as she mouthed it about, he could see the highest branches shaken occasionally as she gave a resistant bit a sharp tug.

Twice he caught a glimpse of black hide through the stems of willow.

Twice he listened to her move to the side away from the opening through which he hoped to kill her; twice he listened to her return but never far enough.

And all the while the bow lay ready in his hands, the arrowhead fastened, the shaft fitted to the string.

88

Indeed, until this closing in, he had not so much as opened the arrow bag.

There were some who would have opened the bag, even taken practice shots with a blunt arrow made for the purpose.

But not so K'Anta. He had no need to open the bag for he knew what shafts and what heads he would find there.

He would not bend this bow, the bow of the hunter made especially for the son, save with the intent to kill.

But the bow would not be bent this day.

The cow did not break cover. Finally, as dusk fell, she moved off into the heavier timber until she was out of the hearing of the hunter.

With as much caution as he had come there, K'Anta withdrew from that place. Then he found a thicket of small spruce around one very large tree. Under this he made his mat of brush and his fire for the night, eating only a little of the dried meat in his small pack.

Chapter 14

At daybreak, he took up the pursuit once more.

First, he verified the wind, confirming that it lay completely still. He would have preferred a slight drift, in any direction.

Then he picked up her trail, following it through the bottom lands of the stream course until he came upon the bed she had made then left again sometime before the dawn.

He pressed between his fingers the balls of dung she had made on rising. Soft yet, they confirmed his belief that in the time since she had lain here he had shortened the distance between them.

She had risen not long before he had risen. She had traveled a little longer than he had traveled.

But she had browsed, and therefore she had moved not so far as he had moved.

For a long while he waited by her bed, screening the sounds of the forest.

Then he moved out to make his first half circle on her trail, but so slowly that he might hardly be moving at all. And he doubted that he would ever complete the half circle.

A long time passed.

He moved by several bits of cover, seeing through several breaks in the willow growth.

Then, in the long interval between putting one foot down and raising the next, he saw her.

In a brief glimpse of the side of her head and an ear as she reached for a high-growing willow shoot, he saw her.

He shrunk himself down to his haunches, then lay forward in the snow.

Slowly, he readied the bow and the first arrow.

Then, on the top of the arrow bag just a little forward and to the right, the next arrow.

Then, because the ground before him obstructed the path of an arrow shot from the surface level of the snow, he drew himself back upon his knees, then crouched low in a position that, while it kept his profile close to the snow, would let him draw the bow and shoot, when the time came, from a little above the ground.

He heard her move, in the ambling gait that accompanied her browsing, into heavier cover.

He spent the next long while shifting himself in order to shoot better from ground level. This also widened his view of the breaks in the cover.

If the cow moved in any direction now but straight away from him, he would see her.

For a long time she hardly moved at all, and K'Anta only knew she remained because he would have heard her had she left.

Then she moved once more, and this time it was to move off, not to shift about again in browsing.

The bow string tightened, drawing the ends of the stave into deep, powerful curves.

The cow continued to move.

K'Anta's forearm, stiffening against the resistance of the wood to further bending, arrested the trembling of the hand.

The cow broke cover, head followed by shoulders.

The hand grew steadier as the bending arm strained to fetch the last of the power of the bow into the string behind the shaft.

The cow stepped clear.

Now.

Into the place where the hide is weakest and the flesh is thin, where the life organs lie least protected.

Now.

The eye fixed the mark and the hand released the shaft.

The cow fled.

K'Anta gathered his arrow bag and slung it on his shoulder, then walked, no longer in caution, to where the cow had been when the arrow struck.

He looked for the blood which would now mark her trail. Seeing it in quantity he walked on to a spruce thicket to break branches for a mat and dry twigs for a fire.

He gave her plenty of time, time to run out her first terror, time to grow exhausted, time to seek a thicket from which she might watch her back trail, time to grow stiff in her bed from the wound, still enlarging from the barbed arrowhead creeping within her.

When he did take up her trail he walked quickly, his eyes picking up the tracks well ahead.

Down through here she ran, full out.

Up this slight rise, for the first time, she slowed down.

Then she ran again, but not so far.

Now she walked.

The blood on the snow grew less. The blood in the wound had clotted. But still she bled, inside.

Soon she will circle, coming back onto her own trail, to watch for pursuit when she is forced to lie down by the loss of the blood inside her.

So K'Anta left her trail, into the ever useful circling pattern again.

The first circle cut the track, a slow track now, searching for cover to lie down in.

The next circle did not cut track, and therefore she lay somewhere within it.

K'Anta tightened the circle.

She could not get up and he drove the arrow into the jugular.

The little blood that remained spilled out on the snow. He touched his finger to the blood in the wound, then passed it to his tongue.

"Forgive me what I have done here, old mother," he said, "but I am only a poor hunter and I need meat for the people in my camp. But I will be careful of your bones, and I will not leave them about to be chewed by the wolves."

92

Chapter 15

Now that he had killed, K'Anta found to his surprise that no particular sensation of feeling accompanied it.

It had been so vastly important to accomplish that he had expected more reaction. In the event, he felt it hadn't really been a first time at all, that there never had been a first time, that he, K'Anta had always been a hunter, had always killed. He who has always been a hunter has always killed; for by killing, he sustains life.

This animal before him on the snow was only one of many, and with his stone knife he butchered her.

He made up a pack load of the meat to carry, then cached the rest, covering it well with brush. The brush would keep off the ravens, the smell of his hands the wolves, even for one night, the wolverine. Tomorrow, the men would fetch it all to camp.

He shouldered the pack, then made his way away from the stream course to the place where he would pick up the main trail. When he reached this, his pace quickened and he neared the camp of his people only a little after dark.

He did not play the game of the returning hunter as he had always planned. Just as his father had not done so all this season, so he chose not to now, for he returned in ceremony as well as in fact, and it would not be appropriate.

He walked into the camp, into the circle of light.

His mother saw him, but she looked away at once for it was not her place.

His uncle saw him and quietly spoke his name.

From somewhere his father appeared beside him and helped him off with the pack.

As his father put the meat in the cache K'Anta put his bow and the arrow bag in the tree, away from the paths of the women, where the hunting weapons of all the men were kept.

Then he went to the fire in the main shelter, hungrily smelling the meat that hung over the flames in the large pot.

His father joined him, fetching out a large piece, passing it to him on his steel knife.

"You are hungry."

"I am hungry. I have eaten little for I did not know how long my small supply might have to last."

"That is the way it is when you hunt. Of course you can set a few snares, but it takes time from the hunting. Well, now you can eat all you want. A good hunter eats little on the trail, but he eats all he wants when he returns."

Those words released K'Anta from the stringent days which had gone before. He ate voraciously of the meat, swelling his belly with it, savoring the flavor of cooked fresh meat after the meager meals of dried meat, eaten cold and in nibbling amounts.

His father joined him, then soon the whole camp came. They had all eaten earlier, but now they ate again and before long the cache was scoured for some fat ribs, which had been put away for a time when it would be good to roast them, glistening before the fire, the fat melting and dripping down as the meat on the bones turned brown and tender.

The whole camp talked freely as the tension of the past days was swept away. The carefree happiness grew as it passed from one to the other, and in K'Anta it glowed like a fire of warm coals in a secure shelter.

The talk was the talk of hunters, about the animals they sought for their livelihood, of the long hard trails of the hunt, of the distant mountains and the nearby valleys, of bad luck and hardship, of good luck and plenty, of hunger and misery, of abundance and joy.

When the hunter kills, happiness follows.

K'Anta, the hunter, the son of a hunter, had killed and there was much happiness.

Particularly, there was happiness for his father.

"I think," he said, after the talk had gone on for a long time and the fire had been built up several more times, "that I might make a little feast of the meat my son has killed."

And there was accord that this was a good plan. Indeed there was much meat in the cache. If some was not given away, the spirits of the animals might easily be offended at this greed.

The talk finally died away and people gathered their robes about them to sleep. K'Anta, for the first time since his father had brought the training to fever pitch, gathered robes about him until he no longer felt the penetration of the cold.

The father, whose thoughts and actions in all that same time had been only for his son, lay beside his wife again.

Chapter 16

The people came for the feast from the nearest camps where word could be sent and stayed for several days.

The older men told stories far into the night, stories of the early times of the people, stories of the power of the animal spirits and the magic by which their power might be exploited by the hunter, stories of hunters who, asking too much of the spirits, were taken by the animal people, to wander in the valleys changed into moose or high on the mountains changed into caribou.

The feasting used up the whole of the cow K'Anta had killed and meat from the cache besides. Then his father further depleted the cache as he gave generously of meat and hides to the Crow people, the people of K'Anta's own moiety.

Then because there were Crow people and Wolf people in each of the visiting camps, he gave some meat to the Wolf people too, so they would not regret the time they had spent coming there.

After the visitors had gone the cache held just about the meat needed to see the camp through, with a little to spare.

The men lost no time getting back to gathering fur. Everyone coveted a steel blade or a cooking pot, and no man now felt his position maintained unless his wife had beads to decorate her sewing. Increasingly, too, they fostered the hope of guns; and the price of these things was fur.

K'Anta trapped with his father, not as an apprentice but as a craftsman now. True, he still watched closely what his father did, largely setting his own deadfalls in the same way. But he used his own ideas, too, and often they worked surprisingly well.

They traveled the same main trail together, but each took his own side trails up tributary draws. The father divided the territory so both had an equal chance of success.

Soon the cache of fur began to grow. K'Anta's fur did not grow quite so quickly as his father's, but quickly enough for him to begin to think of owning his own steel knife blade after the trading time in the summer.

Thinking of the knife, he trapped all the harder. When severe cold set in just after the days had begun to lengthen again he was persuaded not to go out only on his father's assurance that the fur animals wouldn't be moving about enough to get into the deadfalls and snares.

But whenever the weather broke he impatiently waited for his father to decide to go again, and happily complaining that his son must want to trap all the fur in one season, his father readily went out. When the winter was over and the camp moved to the beaver hunting, K'Anta had a pack of fur he could carry to the trade place with pride and some hope that it would buy a knife.

Much excitement surrounded the gathering together after the long winter.

Cousins found each other with joy, pretending not to notice the difference of a winter's growing older.

Fathers met sons, feigning indifference, but anxious to know how the boy had made out in the camp of his in-laws.

Women gathered into the happy company of each other, sharing the joys they couldn't share fully with their menfolk, joys of a newborn child or a son come of age, of a daughter well married or a grandchild pretty as well as useful.

Old One Without Teeth shuffled about the camp offering his pack of furs to mothers, still patiently playing his game while others watched with sadness this spectacle of absurdity still pressing the joke that was no longer a joke.

Into all this K'Anta came, carefree and assured, full of the confidence of having become a hunter, knowing that the story of his success preceded him. Yet he came, too, with respect for his elders, keeping largely silent, for there was no brashness in his self-assurance.

But the life of a hunting people is hard, on the whole, and does not tolerate carefree intervals in the individual spans that comprise it. Men are born and idle in childhood only for a moment: then they are thrust through puberty into the craft by which they must live, thence into marriage and the support of children, soon followed by grandchildren, then eldership and the rapid relinquishment of everything for which, so little time ago, they were born.

K'Anta remained carefree for only a moment.

The stimulation of the gathering and the vigor of his own new manhood swept him on. He responded to the sight and the fragments of voice that reached him of young single women in the other camps.

K'Anta, the young hunter, began to think it would be well to have someone to sew his clothes and tend his fire, to tan the hides of the animals he killed and mend his moccasins.

These were good thoughts for they recognized the essential division of labor between men and women among a hunting people. When K'Anta sat alone on the banks of the creek at the beaver grounds and felt how intensely his young body wanted to sow its seed, responding to the presence of the young women, it made entirely good sense that he thought of his need for clothing and fire making, hide tanning and moccasin mending.

Perhaps this was why at first he did not realize how pretty she was. Her name was Xetsi and she lived in a camp comprised of her mother and father and an older sister whose husband was still fulfilling to his in-laws the obligations that came with marrying the elder of the daughters still in their camp.

There were several even older daughters, but each was now in her own camp with her husband, each of the sons-in-law in turn having lived with the parents until a new son-in-law was acquired through the next of the daughters.

The couple had had no sons, and secretly most people felt that in the old man's improvidence he had brought it upon himself. Perhaps sons simply would not be born where the lack of a good hunter to prepare them was so singularly obvious.

For this old man, this father of daughters, had been improvident in all his life. He had been an uninterested son of his own

98

father, preferring to lean on others right from the beginning. Reluctant to leave the comfort of the camp for the hardships of the trail, he was soon left to it by a father who had other sons who were anxious to learn, sons in whom his pride as a hunter had hope of outliving his own vigor.

Early then, he ate the meat killed by others and it held no shame, it seemed, that he could not kill for his own stomach, much less to help to feed the camp.

He might never have married except that a girl child, orphaned when her parents were swept from a raft in an accident on the river, came into his parents' camp to be cared for.

They were both little wanted, he for his indifference to his calling and the girl very simply because she was another mouth to feed in an already overburdened camp, a camp that had unfortunately accumulated three aged grandparents and a crippled uncle.

Knowing she created a burden, the child fell to with a will though she was not yet a woman by two seasons when she came. She struggled with every task put upon her, bearing the scoldings which followed even her best efforts. By the time she went into the puberty hut, she had gained most of the skills most girls only then begin to learn.

It was not surprising that these two unwanted people joined together. He could never gain a wife on the strength of his hunting: she was without dowry. Though the young hunter must give bride service and, through his parents, a marriage gift, he seeks also through his marriage valuable rights in new hunting ground. As an orphan, she conveyed no rights.

There was no marriage feast or announcement, indeed in the absence of bride service and a gift, how could there be?

The two sought comfort in each other for the inferiority of their position. Their sleeping together marked their union.

One bit of fortune fell their way. He had been one of several sons, but there had been only one daughter. His older brothers had married into distant hunting territory and the sister had gone to her in-law's camp. There was, therefore, room in his father's hunting territory, and they made a camp by themselves in a tributary valley.

It was she who kept them alive. All the people knew that. She worked tirelessly at her woman's chores and had always enough snares out to keep them in food, with at least a little luck.

On top of that, she went with him to set the larger snares so that on occasion they might take a moose or a caribou. He never set a snare alone. When she had to stay in camp at the birth of a child they made out on the rabbits around the camp or the dried meat she had put ahead for the time of need.

They were ever short of hides for clothing, but she kept them going by remaking one garment into another, using the back of a worn-out robe to make moccasins, old leggings into mitts for a baby.

Her industry saved them and all the daughters she bore. Everywhere the people acknowledged it, and the unwanted orphan girl became much respected.

Then through her daughters she secured their later years against the misery that might well have been their lot. She taught them, out of the harshness of her own necessity, every skill of her nimble fingers, every precaution against ill fortune, every saving little way in which the least scrap of food or hide or sinew might be put to use.

As though she must have the reward of her own thrift, just as her husband must lack sons as the punishment due his improvidence, her daughters were singularly attractive. It soon followed, when these same daughters were seen in the beaver camps to be tirelessly at work, hardly raising their eyes, that a succession of young hunters came to winter with this improvident man and his industrious wife, offering bride service in earnest.

Not only must each son-in-law give bride service before marriage, lasting at least a season, each had then to remain until another replaced him.

The services of a hunter in his camp gave Xetsi's father a new occupation beside that of avoiding the hardships of the trail.

With big game coming in, his wife and daughters, the older of whom were as efficient in running a snare line as their mother,

100

could leave the constant pursuit of small game for survival and set deadfalls for fur. Admittedly, this meant intense trapping within a short distance of the camp, but the camp could be relocated yearly so a fresh habitat could be hunted each season.

To add to this store, there was the fur caught by a son-in-law or prospective son-in-law, who, anxious to please in order to achieve his purpose quickly and then be away, wouldn't dispute the old man's claim to the fur.

This supply of fur made Xetsi's father, over the years of his daughters' maturity, a powerful man on the trading ground.

The Tlingit, recognizing one who, rather like themselves, had the skill to exploit the effort of others for more gain than he could reap by his own, sought him out. They competed for trading partnership with him, and this alone added to the leverage of his large fur pack.

It was paradoxical, in fact, that two of the least useful men among all the people usually disposed of the largest amount of fur: Xetsi's father and One Without Teeth.

But it was Xetsi's father who became obsessed with the business of trade. He learned enough of their tongue to harangue the Tlingit in their own fashion. Long after others had settled for what the Tlingit refused to exceed in beads or pots or steel blades, this one man, this failure on the hunting ground, still held out, warily putting out his furs, loudly demanding more in return, skillfully gauging how far the bluff would go, pretending several times in the course of the bargaining that the furs on the ground were his last, only to conclude a deal then fetch more from his shelter to start over again.

He was indeed a man after their own fashion, and the Tlingit took him not for an improvident man living on others, but for a shrewd man, commanding wealth, of influence among his people.

Out of his skill at trading he derived something else: this improvident man without means of entry into the exchange of accomplishment around the fires at night—for who would listen to the empty talk of a man who had never shot a moose or snared a sheep—now had a place, even if grudgingly acknowledged.

When others told of killing a caribou on a far mountain when

101

the life of the camp hung on it, he told of besting the Tlingit for another knife blade after they thought they had all his fur by bringing out of hiding a few more pelts, haranguing over them half the night.

Even at the hard prices of the Tlingit, he gained, by trading, more steel blades and other goods than his camp could use.

But this gave him another opportunity. Every couple was expected to return the generosity of bride service and a marriage gift with something of special use to their new son-in-law: an outfit of clothing, a new and handsome hunting pack or, in these days of trade, perhaps something gained from the Tlingit.

The generosity of this giving measured the couple who gave. Those who gave in niggardly fashion, did so at a loss in prestige. Those who gave well might look down for a long time afterward on those who hadn't.

Now the husband of the orphan woman, the father of daughters, could give well, and the fact that his gifts came from trading the furs caught by others, even partly by those very sons-in-law to whom he gave, could not pare away the importance of the giving.

For the people suffered a little, too, from the grand obsession of the Tlingit with symbols of wealth, and those who could afford to give away wealth could not be denied the prestige to which this entitled them.

So Xetsi's father had come by way of the trading ground into a position denied him when he had only his manhood by which to be measured.

Still it was precariously held. It hung on a continuing supply of furs, and as the daughters married and took their skills elsewhere, the prestige had to be won by increasing tenacity in the bargaining. But this had its limits. On the horizon, as the camp grew small again, lay the prospect of insufficient fur to maintain what had been so hard bought.

When the camp went down to just the old couple, Xetsi, and perhaps the hunter who would be drawn in by her nubility, would there be enough fur?

But not all this was seen by K'Anta.

Instead he saw the nimble fingers hard at work, the ready hands always busy and the quick movements of an efficient girl, not quite his age, but already over the threshold into womanhood.

He soon exploited his acquaintance with the young hunter married to her older sister to come casually into Xetsi's camp. He could sit by the fire then, within a pace or two of the girl whose eyes never turned from her work, to chat idly with his friend and observe this strange relationship between this garrulous old man and his quiet forceful wife who had come out of orphanhood so long ago K'Anta couldn't imagine it, this unlikely couple and the silent, busy girl.

He could not like her father. Yet he gave the old man courtesy, listening to his boastful talk of trading, puzzling how a man could be anything if not a hunter. He found himself estimating how one might put up with him, without quite admitting that the only way it could be necessary would be in the attempt to become the last of his sons-in-law.

Xetsi's mother was different altogether. She reminded K'Anta of his own mother, and he wondered how different life might have been for her if she had not been shorn of her kinships so early. With a mother to hold out for a hunter worthy of her skills, surely she would have been the mother of sons, as surely an industrious woman deserves to be.

His visits to their camp under the guise of his friendship, a friendship genuine in itself, grew in frequency. Often he sat before their fire until late in the evening, pretending to be uninterested in Xetsi as indeed he felt any hunter would pretend to be uninterested in any woman, but staying, nonetheless, until after she had left her place by the fire and gone to the seclusion of the shelter.

He never exchanged a word with her.

During the days he hunted with his father and they caught many beaver for the greasy meat they loved so well and the hides they stretched and dried so the women might work them later in the season.

Once he made a mistake because his mind was away from his work. He and his father lay in a blind, waiting for beaver to surface in a pond where they had only begun to hunt. They had decided against snares, proposing to shoot with arrows only the occasional beaver that might come out to the banks for saplings.

When a beaver appeared K'Anta shot much too soon, forgetting what he was about, and the animal tumbled back in the water to be swept down by the current.

They retrieved it, but not until they had run downstream and both been soaked in the task.

They had to return to camp, for it would be impossible in wet clothing to lie in the blind for the hours needed for another beaver to appear. So the error had cost the day's hunting as well as the discomfort.

K'Anta felt terrible shame and knew not what to say. But his father's understanding even yet surpassed K'Anta's perception of its depth. As he set about skinning the beaver after he had changed his clothes his father came to help, kneeling beside him.

A time passed in which the wordless reassurance, which always reached from the father to the son, wiped away the discomfort of the shame.

Then: "It is good to visit in the camps when we are all together like this. It is how we know each other after the long winter. But not so much that people might talk."

After that K'Anta stayed in his parents' camp a little more in the evenings, keeping his mind on his work and planning his visits to Xetsi's camp so he could still see something of her without it being so obvious. Indeed, in his own mind his visits now seemed acutely so.

Chapter 17

All too soon the camps broke up and disbanded to the lakes for the net fishing that would last until trading time.

Several individual camps would still make up a fishing camp but not in the grand collection of all the people, which happened only at beaver time and later at trading time.

Xetsi's parents joined no one. They had no rights, fishing only by sufferance a shallow bay scorned by others on a remote lake.

So K'Anta found a new pain now. No longer did he suffer simply the hunger of his manhood for a woman, but now the agony of having found the only woman to meet his need and she, being the only one, had multiplied the pain a thousandfold.

It was the pain of love, which knows not what to do or how to proceed.

He had never had a word with her. He had no idea of her feelings. Although when a hunter chose a wife it was for him to ask and her mother to grant or refuse, he couldn't escape the uncertainty over how she felt.

Suppose the continual averting of her eyes was more than the natural reticence toward a young hunter from another camp? Suppose she preferred that he would not come, or was it that she thought him only there because he liked to talk with her brother-in-law at the fireside?

Maybe she couldn't regard him seriously anyway. He was hardly older than she herself was. He had only made his first kill this season past, and while much had been made of his beginning as a hunter, it was still a beginning. Fully a woman and ready to bear children, she was entitled to the interest of accomplished hunters many years older, and might regard K'Anta as little more than a boy.

Was this not the real meaning of the far-away look, the eyes that never left the task at hand?

And what if another, older and more certain than K'Anta should seek her? He would surely succeed, for how could parents in her position refuse? Perhaps already there was one who had made such a decision, who was so certain of success he had no need to let his actions betray his intent, no need to hang around the old fool's camp for all the people to see.

Then K'Anta would wish painfully that he had kept his distance, that he had given more thought to how he must have looked to the others, forever finding excuses to sit at that one campfire.

His father could not help him now. Indeed, K'Anta was so anxious that his father should not know the anguish he suffered that he sought in every way to hide it. Bravely, his heart in turmoil, he went about his work in the fishing as faithfully as his father expected.

But he could hardly wait for the gathering at the trade place to begin. It was no longer the cherished dream of a steel knife blade that drew him there, but the certainty that she would be there, too, that he would see her again. Thinking of this, he told himself it would be enough just to see her once more. Somehow, he thought, if I might see her just once more, it will not matter what happens after. I might never see her again, she might marry another and go to some distant place, but it will be bearable if I can see her just once more.

Eventually the time came, and the people gathered at the trade place amidst much talk that this year the Tlingit should bring guns, that it was no longer fair to take the furs away without bringing guns.

When K'Anta saw her the pain that shot him through made nonsense of his resolution that to see her one more time was all he needed. His agony became greater than before.

But so also did his pride come to his rescue. He controlled himself with resolve, going only into her camp to the extent that courtesy called on him to visit where before he had spent such quantities of time. Whatever the misery of this terrible attraction, this emotion whose existence hadn't even been imagined before Xetsi, K'Anta determined that he would not bare his feelings before others, and he didn't.

The Tlingit arrived just as the men began to wonder if they could wait any longer before moving into the salmon camps.

After a day of ceremony and feasting the trading began, and once more the hopes of the people for guns were frustrated. A little anger crept into the insistence of the Athabascans, a little truculence into the arrogance of the Tlingit. Men like K'Anta's father, who knew the danger of this hostility, did their best to put it down and the trading went on.

The Tlingit, sensing the limits to which they had pressed the people, eased their prices a little, giving a steel blade and a cooking pot where before they might have given but one or the other.

Glad of this, the people stopped pressing for the guns, but later some were even more angry that they had been bought off so lightly.

K'Anta left his own trading till the last, watching the others to learn what he could before taking his own first steps in something new.

He saw how the Tlingit held back until certain a man had put out all his furs; how, even when they made concessions in price because of the feeling over the absence of guns, they retained control.

He watched how the older partnerships traded quickly and how the newer ones took time, each side searching for advantage. He saw that when the bargaining started there was a formality of adjustments to go through before agreement could be reached, even though he was certain more than once that the agreement had been understood before the bargaining began.

When the men in established partnership had completed trading, the others had to feel their way toward each other as best they could, so K'Anta put his pack of furs on the ground before him.

A young Tlingit came forward, putting down a steel-bladed knife.

It was a good knife, as nearly as K'Anta could tell from what he had seen of knives.

He took the furs from his pack, laying them out to be easily seen and reckoned.

He studied the face of the other then and recognized him as the younger member of the Tlingit camp of Xetsi's father's trading partner.

The young Tlingit handled the furs and a feeling of antagonism, a little surprising to K'Anta, stirred inside him. But he kept it to himself.

The Tlingit stepped back, waiting.

K'Anta puzzled a moment, then gathered that the furs were not enough. He wished he knew the Tlingit tongue, and the antagonism stirred a little harder.

Uncertain what to do, he became intensely conscious of the eyes that watched them, the eyes of the Tlingit and the eyes of the people. Some would be much amused at these two youngsters trading for the first time. Perhaps others would not be so amused.

But were the Tlingit not always amused at the expense of the Athabascans?

K'Anta met the eyes of the young Tlingit, perhaps a few years his senior, no more, and he saw there a touch of mockery, a half-smile that flickered with contempt.

The antagonism turned to hatred and K'Anta controlled himself, even in his confusion, as the hunter controls himself when his heart beats wildly and his hand trembles.

He knew suddenly his mistake: that he should have held back some fur that he could go for now, to give the Tlingit the face of winning, of having bettered him in the bargaining.

But it was too late for that. All his fur lay on the ground before him. And he no more knew what to do than he had fur left to offer.

The knife and the fur lay on the ground and K'Anta silently spoke his contempt of himself for having failed to foresee this. He had had chances enough to learn from others.

Past the smirk of the Tlingit before him he caught sight of his father who had moved to the Tlingit side of the bargaining ground.

108

Their eyes met and his father walked by him toward their camp.

Not sure why, but certain his father intended it, he followed. When they reached their own camp, his father passed him a few furs, all that remained of his father's pack—in fact, held back in case this difficulty should confront either of them.

When K'Anta put the additional furs beside his own, the Tlingit moved the knife toward him.

The deal was made. K'Anta took the knife and the Tlingit the fur. But the elation he had expected on possession of the steel knife was not there.

Instead, he hated the Tlingit.

Chapter 18

K'Anta determined to speak to Xetsi now that the trading camp was to break up, so he again used his friendship with her brother-in-law to visit her camp.

But he had no idea how to see her alone, nor what he would say if he did so, and miserable but hiding it, he sat by the fire making his talk with the others.

His thoughts were not on the hides she would tan or the clothes she would sew. He saw now the gently molded figure, the strong yet slender hands, the small feet in pretty moccasins, and his dreams were to possess them all.

She sat quietly working, her eyes steadfast on the quick movements of her needle, only a pace from K'Anta with the others by the fire yet she might have been beyond a distant mountain for all the access he had to her.

The evening grew late, though there was no darkness at this time of year. Still, he must return to his father's camp for in the morning they would leave, to return to the salmon camp at the mouth of the tributary river over which his father held rights.

Then, as though she knew his thoughts that now he must leave, in the last opportunity there was for it, she looked up and met his eyes.

It lasted the briefest moment, that first communication between them, and K'Anta had barely recovered from the shock of it when it was over.

Then, desperate to hide his tremors and anxious about whether others had seen, he rose hurriedly to make his leave.

Later he tortured himself with the thought that leaving so quickly he might have conveyed a wrong impression to her, that

110

he disapproved of her boldness, that she was mistaken in thinking his visit was really for her.

But there was nothing he could do to straighten it out, to tell her how he really felt, that all his visits had been for her.

But did she care? After all, it was the briefest glance, a little curiosity perhaps, not necessarily more. If she cared, she would surely have given a sign earlier when there had been time for something more.

And so, having waited so anxiously for some little sign, K'Anta received it, only to have it magnify his doubts.

The next morning they left for the salmon camp and K'Anta threw himself into the hard work that awaited them there.

Then later they returned to the hunting grounds, to take up the pursuit that pleased them most: hunting the large animals, the women drying the meat where the men killed it in the first of the season, later settling into the main camp where the men would pack the meat home in great loads to be frozen by the encroaching frosts.

K'Anta killed well, but satisfaction eluded him. K'Anta, the hunter, son of a hunter, hunted but cared little for it.

Finally, he knew he must do as he knew others had done before him: he must go to offer bride service to the mother of the girl of his choice in the uncertain hope that he might be accepted.

He had given himself hope with the thought that since Xetsi's father was such a failure as a hunter, his own yet fresh skill would seem all the more valuable, but he abandoned that hope now that he thought seriously of his chances. It was Xetsi's mother whose judgment must be met, and she would have no illusions about her husband or what kind of son-in-law she wanted by comparison. If anything, her luck in her own husband would make her more demanding, not less.

He wished that he were two seasons readier to ask his father what he now must ask him.

But he put himself to it and he did not, he thought, betray his uncertainty. He chose a time when they were alone, in an overnight bivouac at a kill they had made.

"My father, I am young yet, but I think I should seek a wife."

111

In the silence K'Anta waited in the way he had learned. The older man poked the fire with a stick for a long thoughtful while, then threw it on the blaze and spoke.

"I will show you the way to her camp. But you know that you may not be accepted? Yes, you are young yet."

K'Anta recovered from the discovery that his father had already dealt with questions he hadn't put.

"Yes," he said, "I know I may not be accepted. But it will do no harm to hunt for them a season. Can you let me go?"

"Yes. I can let you go. And your mother and I will make the marriage gift for you, too, if the time comes." Then after a pause: "You seek a large burden, but I know you cannot help it."

How large a burden frightened him when he realized it some time later, after Xetsi's brother-in-law, grasping the chance to be released from that burden himself, left the camp only a few days after K'Anta arrived.

His mind made up, he had lost no time in getting on with the dictates of his heart. His father had traveled the first two days with him, then given him directions for the remainder of the journey.

Little had been said on his arrival. Indeed, others had come before on a similar journey, seeking the older sisters. K'Anta had flushed in brief and secret anger when the realization struck him that probably they had counted on his coming, only wondering when.

He had come in at dusk, walking into the firelight to be recognized.

"You come a long journey." It was the son-in-law who had spoken and K'Anta had been grateful, for it had saved him the awkward task of explaining himself.

"Yes, I come a long journey."

It had been easy after that to take a place by the fire and accept food, to see Xetsi as always a little back from the others, to fall into talk that had no reference to his own arrival. Later, Xetsi's mother had taken his robe from his pack, spreading it in a corner of the brush shelter he might have for himself. He had found when he went there to sleep that she had given him an extra robe to go with the light one he had used on his journey.

It was the following morning that his intentions had been drawn from him, skillfully, to save him embarrassment.

Xetsi's mother managed it.

"You have come to stay with us a while?"

"Yes. I had thought I might."

"We do not mind. Of course you will want to hunt for us for we have a hard time here. Our ground is poor for game and my husband's luck has not been good. Our son-in-law here helps us, but it is difficult, all the same."

"I will hunt for you."

There, it had been done. The simple pledge made: I will hunt for you. And unspoken but understood lay the rest of it: if I hunt well, my parents will make a marriage gift, and if you are satisfied, you will accept it and Xetsi will be my wife and I will hunt yet awhile for you after that, and for the rest of your life I shall share with all your sons-in-law the obligation to see you through, never to leave you in hardship.

For the first time since arriving then he had looked directly toward Xetsi. As if she sensed it she had glanced toward him with an inscrutable, half-whimsical glance, nearly but not quite smiling, and uncertainty had stirred up all the turmoil within him once again.

It had been as well that the man who he hoped would one day be his brother-in-law had lost no time in putting them both on the hunting trails.

There had followed a few intense days of hunting, days in which they traveled far but killed only once, a bull that had all but run them down in the distraction of the rut.

They might have killed much more, indeed they might have killed a winter's meat for a small camp, but they had never slowed the pace enough, walking rapidly on through fresh sign even when it lay thick about them.

K'Anta had puzzled on this for it was no way to hunt. But now he understood, now that the older hunter had left with his wife to return to the camp of his own people.

It had been two seasons since he had come on the same journey as K'Anta, to offer bride service for the older sister. He had hunted for them one season before the marriage and one season since. His obligation kept him until another took his place.

Even K'Anta now understood the hurry of his leaving: he must go before there was any danger of K'Anta changing his mind.

Well K'Anta might have, but for the emotion that impelled him. Though the hunter who seeks a wife expects to hunt in the service of his in-laws, he does not expect to carry the camp singlehanded.

So here was the explanation for the fact that K'Anta had not really been hunting during those few days of rushing about the ground of his prospective in-laws. Rather, he had been getting a fast look at the limited territory out of which he must now make a living for the four remaining people.

Young K'Anta, one season after his first kill, held the lives of three others and himself in his own two hands.

As he lay in his robes the night this had become plain to him, he tried to recapture the exhilaration of the days of the previous season when his only hunger had been to hunt and, hunting, he had easily satisfied it.

But it would not come back. Now he yearned in an intense inexplicable way, and the object of it all was the bit of a girl who lay in her own robes but a few feet away in another part of the camp.

Now he would hunt in deadly earnest because they all must live by his skill alone, but there would be nothing in it for K'Anta if at the end of it, his skill did not give him Xetsi.

K'Anta took stock.

It was late fall and there was only the meat of the bull they had just killed, a remnant of an earlier kill, a little dried meat and even less dried fish.

By contrast, there was plenty of women's food: dried berries, roots and, already, rabbits coming in occasionally from the snare line.

But this was not enough if the late winter became severe.

K'Anta wondered if there was another cache but abandoned the hope before asking. Still, it seemed odd there should be so

114

little, for while Xetsi had an improvident father, her brother-in-law had seemed perfectly capable. Then with a little more thought, K'Anta saw the explanation for that. The brother-in-law, weary of his position in this beggaring camp, had read the signs of K'Anta's affliction, having suffered it himself so recently, and had known that he was about to be relieved. Accordingly, his exertions had slackened off.

K'Anta went hunting.

The bulls were full in the rut and while he would have scorned their meat by now in his father's camp, he took advantage of the ease of calling the frenzied animals into range, and killed three in rapid succession.

Fortunately, he had not had to go far from camp for this initial success; for not only did Xetsi's father not hunt, neither did he trouble himself to pack meat.

So K'Anta packed meat until Xetsi and her mother had two racks full drying, then left the rest for these willing women to carry in while he set off for more.

And at last, in this essential activity of the life of the camp, some little association with Xetsi became possible. True, her mother was always there but that was only right. But Xetsi was standing by, not apart, when K'Anta agreed with her mother that these first kills should be dried, though the season was late for drying and it would take a lot of fire. The bull meat would lose some of its rankness in drying, and some dry meat might be badly wanted in the early spring before beaver time.

There she was, too, cutting the meat and hanging it as soon as he came in with a first pack, and he had occasion to help her reinforce one side of the uprights that supported the rack.

He trembled at her nearness, but the importance of their tasks helped him bear it, and the earlier misery ebbed away as she came out of the remoteness of that silent person always on the outer edge of the circle around the fire.

He discovered, in fact, that she was an ordinary person like other people and, far from diminishing his love of her, this reinforced it, giving him hope, easing his heart.

K'Anta did not kill again for quite a few days. He had trouble

115

locating fresh sign, then when he did he had bad luck with the first two cows he stalked. They walked out of range without breaking cover.

He had begun to wonder if he shouldn't set snares, even though he would need time to make the snares and saw little material around the camp for doing it. But his luck changed and he killed a cow, then in a few more days another one.

He had made the camp secure. Though they would eat heartily of it and, indeed, they would eat little else nor wish to, there was meat enough to see them through.

He would kill again, of course, but probably after the snow that would come any day now, which was already overdue.

The three of them packed in the cow meat, and this was strange for K'Anta, this companionship with women. In his father's camp, the men would kill and the women would come to dry the meat and take it in, while the men went on with hunting. Or, when the meat was to be carried fresh to camp, the men would take in the first loads then leave the rest to the women.

But here there were only the three of them, and they must all work together to secure the meat after each of K'Anta's kills.

Still, it was companionable. K'Anta liked the older woman who was much like his mother in her hard-working imperturbable way. He enjoyed the jesting relationship he was entitled to have with her, which would have to disappear when he became her son-in-law.

"Hurry, old mother," he would say. "We must get this meat in before I lose my patience and kill another cow."

"If you kill another cow before this one is all in the cache, we'll leave you to pack it alone."

"Oh, no, mother, you couldn't. I should grow so weary of it, I would leave the hides in the bush and what would you do then?"

"I wouldn't have to scrape hides all winter. That would be fine."

But none of this joking hid the joy of the older woman that she now had hides to work, and a little of K'Anta's old happiness returned as the fruits of his hunting brought industry and pleasure into the camp.

116

For it was the meat he killed and the hides he secured which busied the hands of the girl he loved and her worthy old mother together.

The old man was a different matter, best ignored. He lay about the camp, sleeping as much in the day time as at night. He did no work, complaining if enough weren't done for him. He wouldn't so much as keep the fire going—except when he was alone and would grow cold if he didn't. When the rest returned from bringing in meat, he complained that they had been gone so long he'd had to fetch wood.

He used his eternal presence by the fire to take the choicest bits of meat out of the cooking pot for himself, while K'Anta, hungry from the trail food of only a bit of dried meat and the odd rabbit he'd snared, had only the second best left to choose from. Then the old shirker would bore him with stories of his prowess on the trading ground, offering unbelievable excuses for not going out on the hunting trail.

He had a bad back and a bad foot. His stomach ailed him and his breath was short. Little did people realize how much he suffered in the night, unable to sleep. How lucky K'Anta was that he could sleep at night. It was a terrible affliction, not being able to sleep.

Finally, in secret disgust, K'Anta would leave the fire he would dearly have enjoyed if he could have shared it with another hunter, to wrap himself in his robes in his corner of the shelter.

K'Anta set a few deadfalls for fur with encouraging luck. Then when the snow arrived he killed two more moose, both dry cows.

The camp was no longer only secure, it was fortified with abundance. As it is in the hunting life, it was hard to imagine, when good times attended, how easily hard times and starvation might also come.

With a full meat cache, there is strength and laughter: strength with which to go about the work of living, to dress the hides and sew the clothing, to clean the camp and gather fuel, to tend the snares and make new robes from the rabbit fur, to set deadfalls for the fur animals and dress the pelts; and laughter to make joy of everything.

117

So little stands between this and the misery of starvation. It is only a matter of failing to kill.

Perhaps the hunter does not quite have the skill and without a little extra luck, he doesn't succeed. He comes close, but that is not enough.

Or he has the skills, but he hunts with an unfortunate companion who makes mistakes at crucial moments.

Or the moose are not where he expects to find them, and it is too late by the time he traces their shift in habitat.

The dried fish, used too hard, run out and the rabbits are on the wane, as every few seasons they are.

Hunger afflicts the camp. The hunter, discouraged and weakening, is even more likely to fail now that so much hangs on success.

Hunger turns into starvation.

There is no joy. The women do not work the hides on the stretching frame and the children do not play.

One kill, one fortunate kill by the desperate hunter would change it all, turn the people up the path again instead of down.

Two kills, perhaps three, and strength and gladness will quickly return, and the encouraged hunter may go on succeeding where before he failed.

In the life of a hunting people it is all a matter of killing.

And K'Anta had killed with great success, delivering the means of strength and gladness into the little camp that depended upon him.

In the first flush of his success K'Anta could not believe, as Xetsi's mother had told him, that their ground was poor.

But by the time he had assured the security of the camp for the winter, he had accepted the truth of what she said. For in those few kills, he had been over the whole of the territory, the limited bottom land and surrounding low hills of one small stream, tributary to a still limited creek that joined another before joining the big river.

This was a little-used corner of Xetsi's grandfather's territory. In his disappointment with this son who wouldn't become a hunter, he had let him live there, where he and his orphan wife might be out of sight.

K'Anta had only his father's hunting ground to compare it with, but the conclusion was inescapable. This ground, too small to harbor all the game needed to support a camp, depended on good luck to bring enough game through it at the necessary season.

So in one season, like this, it would give up all the meat the camp could use. In another, only a scattering of moose in all the rut might pass through, much less remain to winter.

If this was a hunting ground, K'Anta's father controlled many hunting grounds, and indeed K'Anta felt much assured to know that when he married Xetsi he might fall back on his rights in his father's ground when this one failed.

But failure and privation, hunger and misery, had not been their lot in this season, and K'Anta was free now for pursuits other than food.

Chapter 19

Young men in love forever assess their progress, reckon again their chances, wonder how they are doing.

K'Anta was no different except that in these northern forests it was the mother whose mind one had to worry about, since hers was the answer which mattered. How did he measure up in the ways that mattered with Xetsi's mother?

After all, Xetsi had lost that remoteness which had pained him at the start. He had come to know her well in the ordinary ways of the camp, and he had words with her often, words of no consequence, spoken in the presence of others, about meat or firewood or how cold the night or deep the snow.

Still, occasionally, he would turn toward her unexpectedly and catch that fleeting look she gave, with the smile that wasn't quite a smile, and while it still unsettled him it didn't turn him upside down the way it once had done.

But he remained utterly in the dark as to what it could possibly mean.

No, it was now a question of Xetsi's mother, for whatever Xetsi meant in that look, which said so little yet seemed to mean so much, if her mother accepted the marriage gift, Xetsi would surely accept K'Anta when she knew at last how impossible it would be for him to live without her.

So how did he fare?

Xetsi's mother, above all, would want her daughter to marry a good hunter.

K'Anta had shown himself to be that.

She would want him to have good rights in ground besides their own.

K'Anta had rights in his father's ground, widely known to be excellent ground.

She would want to be certain Xetsi married a hunter who would meet his obligation to care for her and her husband in their old age.

Surely K'Anta had shown his good faith.

K'Anta grew confident.

But he did not lounge about the camp resting on good fortune.

He set out to gather all the fur the limited ground might give, and because it was better fur ground than anything else, he did surprisingly well.

He found he could cover the entire area with four trails, each of which he would travel in rotation, resetting the deadfalls and bringing in the catch.

Each trail took about three days to cover, so he saw all his deadfalls often enough to keep them working but not so often there wasn't time for anything to be caught.

He skinned the fur at night in his trail camps or in a day between trips at the main camp.

The pile of fur began to grow and his thoughts turned to what it might bring at the trading place. His experience with the Tlingit still rankled and he could not think of trading without a flush of anger, but like all the people he valued highly the goods the Tlingit brought from the coast. Perhaps part of his anger was that he wished he did not value quite so highly something for which he had to depend upon others.

Then the question arose in his mind that perhaps he wouldn't be trading this coming season in any case. This hinged on who owned the fur he caught. Was it really his?

What answered that was that anything he might do to add to the certainty of being accepted as a son-in-law, he would rather do than trade with the Tlingit.

So he would give his fur to his father-in-law. But was it his to give? It came from the old man's ground so maybe that settled the question. He didn't want to make a fool of himself by appearing to make a gift to the old man of something the old man already owned by right.

121

He solved the problem simply by leaving all the fur he caught in the cache, making no mention of the subject.

As the catch grew, so also did the old man's interest until finally he was calculating its worth on the trading ground.

With that question settled, K'Anta trapped with increasing determination, believing he could do nothing better in what remained of the season than add to his prospective father-in-law's trading wealth.

By the time the winter had passed, the old man had a magnificent pack of fur, Xetsi's brief glances had given way to shy smiles, easily given, her mother joked freely with K'Anta, though always on the safest of subjects, and K'Anta felt his marriage to be a foregone conclusion. He now waited only for the gathering of the people at the beaver camp so that he might ask his parents to make the marriage gift.

They traveled there as soon as the ice began to open in the ponds.

K'Anta joined his father's camp at once and explained his hopes. They must have expected it. A marriage gift of many hides, soft and finely tanned, along with the best of the fur had already been set aside.

The only words were words of caution in K'Anta's cause.

"You are sure? One winter is a short time."

Bride service could last two years, seldom less than one. Still, K'Anta's confidence, built on the success of his hunting and the genuine need of the old couple for him, pressed him on.

"It is a short time, but I am sure."

"Well then, we will offer the marriage gift."

It had once been the custom to deliver the gift publicly, perhaps to forestall refusal, but in K'Anta's grandfather's time a change had occurred and now the parents might go first and tell of the gift, to see if it would be accepted. Then if it wasn't, everyone was saved embarrassment.

K'Anta waited while his parents went to Xetsi's camp.

He was unprepared for the shock they brought on their return.

The gift was refused.

They did not want K'Anta as a husband to Xetsi.

122

Chapter 20

The shock gave way to anger, then to grief, but he held himself together.

His mother left the two of them, the father and the son, and they waited a while before speaking.

Then: "May I ask them why?" Love turned away is desperate for answers, hungers after explanations.

"It has been a heavy shame for us."

In those words K'Anta saw his father's sorrow: the sorrow that he should have chosen a girl who, through no fault of her own, had so much burden and so little advantage in her kinship; the sorrow that K'Anta must assume such burdens on account of his choice; now the sorrow that they must accept refusal from this of all camps.

This was the worst; for once K'Anta had made his decision, the sorrow of the burdens could be accepted, but the shame of the refusal could not.

His father did not need to say any more. K'Anta understood, and would not shame him further by going groveling into the other camp.

But he determined to see Xetsi secretly, somehow, to secure the answers he had to have if he was to bear his disappointment at all.

So he set to work again with his father, and all the while he waited an opportunity.

She must have had a similar intention, for otherwise it couldn't have happened. One night after darkness had fallen, the lingering last darkness before the season without it, he walked, as he often did, along the path by her camp to the riverbank.

As he had come to do now, he sat on the bank away from all the camps but closer to hers than any, where he could see the flickering light from the fire where he knew she would be.

This night she came to the same place, kneeling on the ground beside him.

"Xetsi! Do they know you are here?"

"Of course not."

K'Anta took time to recover from his surprise. Now he had the opportunity, he was afraid to use it. But she waited and when he found his voice again he had also found the questions that had raged in his mind for days.

"Why will they not have me?"

"It is not for me to say."

"But you must know! Xetsi, I cannot live without you. You must know! You have to tell me."

"Is that true?"

"Is what true?" She was but an arm's length away and he trembled all over. She had never been so near and his mind swam with his questions all out of order. He couldn't think.

"That you cannot live without me."

Then he caught hold again. "I cannot live without you," he repeated. Then the question again: "Why did your mother refuse the gift?"

"It is not for me to say. Why do you not ask her yourself?"

"I cannot." But he couldn't add that it was his pride and his father's pride that prevented him, that they could not bring themselves to ask explanations for a refusal that had come from those whom they wouldn't have bothered to notice if he, K'Anta, had not fallen desperately in love with this bit of a girl.

"Is it your wish, Xetsi?"

"No. It is not my wish. But it is not my wish that matters. It is for my mother to decide."

Then again: "Why has she refused?"

"It is not my mother. It is my father."

"Your father!" It was unbelievable.

It was unbelievable that he would refuse the prospect of a young and vigorous hunter to bind in a kinship obligation that would last

124

the rest of his life, and unbelievable that his wife, who had carried him when there was no one else and would have to do so again, would let him take the decision from her. Still, while it was the mother's decision, all men had the right to tell their women what to decide if they wished. But surely not this man and not this woman.

"If your mother wishes it, why does she not accept? What right has he?"

"He is her husband."

"But he has not kept her, she has kept him. He is a fool!" It broke out of him with terrible feeling.

"Do not speak of him so. My mother had no one and he took her. She has not forgotten."

"Why, then, does he not accept? That is what I must know."

"He wants to have kinship with the Tlingit. I am the only way."

The idea so staggered K'Anta that though he opened his mouth, no words came out. He swallowed, then waited. To be refused had been painful, but it was nothing against the thought of Xetsi being married into the coast people.

But it was impossible. The conviction of that restored him. The Tlingit were said to have married women from the interior closer to the coast to help in their trading, but it had not happened yet among K'Anta's people. And why Xetsi? Surely a Tlingit would want to marry the daughter of an important man with rights in large hunting grounds and many sons to trap the fur.

"But why would the Tlingit . . ." and he stopped himself short, starting again. "I want to marry you because I cannot live without you, because you are a good woman and you know your work. But the Tlingit marry among the people for trade, and your father's ground is small and he has no sons."

"They do not know his ground is small. And he has many sons through his daughters, and some hold rights in good ground."

Only vaguely, K'Anta could see what might be the old man's scheme. Certainly through his daughters' marriages he had gained wide kinship rights; how wide and how compelling K'Anta was yet too inexperienced in the social conventions of his own people to be certain.

125

There was no doubting, either, the strength of position he had achieved through the trading.

Could it be true that if he added to these advantages that of kinship with the Tlingit, he would secure himself on both sides, making many peoples' trade go through his hands?

K'Anta's mind boggled at these thoughts. In the half-lit realizations, he began to see that power and strength did not belong only to the hunter. It was said, he remembered, that many of the Tlingit never hunted any more, that they lived entirely by their trading. And some of the older men, too, said that if the people went on as they were, thinking about nothing all winter but trading time and how to use the words of the Tlingit instead of their own language, before they knew it they'd all be acting like Tlingits, trying to be something they weren't, as if it were not good enough just to be themselves.

But why must all this interfere with K'Anta, who had given good bride service, who had proved his worth as a hunter and who deserved, as a hunter, a woman from among his people? What right had the Tlingit?

He narrowed his thoughts to something he could put into words. "Does he hope to be rich by it?"

"I have heard him say it many times. He says he will be rich if he marries me into the Tlingit."

"And how will he find this son-in-law among the Tlingit who will marry the daughter of a man who cannot hunt and must be cared for by others?"

Her reply flashed back: "If I bring such a burden, why do you care that you are refused?"

"Because I love you."

"Do you not think a Tlingit might love me, too?"

He had angered her. Not knowing why, he became angry, too, in the frustration of this bewildering tangle.

"The Tlingit marry for trade, not for love."

"A wise hunter does not marry for love, either. He marries for a strong back and quick fingers. He marries for the hard work he will put on his wife. You said it yourself."

"I didn't. I said . . ." But he let that go because he was no longer certain what he had said. Then after a long time: "Is there a man already, among the Tlingit?"

"There is one with whose uncle my father says it is arranged. He says it was arranged last season, and it will be done this trading time. He hopes for a gun for a marriage gift."

"Who among the Tlingit?"

"The one you traded with for your knife."

His rage engulfed him and he clenched his fists, then pressed them against his face with his head down.

What a fool they had made of him. They had taken his service without any intention of accepting him. They had lived and lived well on the meat he had killed, and that contemptible and tiresome fool now had furs to trade that he'd never have had but for K'Anta.

"You knew all the time! Your mother knew all the time!" He threw it at her.

"It is not our wish. It was never our wish."

"But you knew all the time I was there."

She put her hands over her face and her body convulsed, but K'Anta did not perceive it.

"You knew all the time," he repeated.

"Yes," she replied weakly. "But we thought he would give it up. We hoped he would give it up."

But he barely heard her. His memory had dredged up the arrogance in the face of the Tlingit who had embarrassed him on the trading ground, and his senses were smothered in hatred.

He could not remember afterwards which one of them had first got up and left.

Chapter 21

The idea came to him almost at once, but many days passed before he could persuade himself it would be right to carry it out.

It was magnificently simple: he would slip into Xetsi's camp and take away her father's fur.

Without the fur, he could never face the Tlingit. He would have to send some face-saving excuse, then go up the river to the salmon camps. Others had done it when their season's catch was too little to be displayed without provoking the amusement of the coastal traders.

K'Anta wouldn't keep the fur. He would return it after the trade time passed, but he would have a whole season in which to find some way out of his predicament. True, he would anger the old man who would inevitably guess who had tricked him, even if K'Anta returned the fur as secretly as he had taken it away. But unless he prevented Xetsi's camp from reaching the trading ground, everything was lost anyway.

He never doubted the scheme would work. He only feared it wouldn't be right—even though he had been sorely wronged, even though he had himself caught by far the bulk of the fur, even though he intended to return it.

The obligations of an aspiring son-in-law are strong, and it does not follow that he is owed anything back for his trouble if, after a time of hunting for the parents of the girl he hopes to win they decide against him.

But he knew the turn of her face and the glance of her eyes too well now: he saw them in the Tlingit camp no matter how he tried to shut his mind to it, or to the fact that if she incited this desire in him, she must surely incite it in others as well, the Tlingit included. The thought of a passion for Xetsi lurking behind the mocking eyes of the Tlingit who had faced him over his furs, seared him, time and again.

Eventually the camps moved to the lakes and not long after, K'Anta, finishing his rationalization, made his decision.

Then he simply left his father's camp without explanation except to say he would be back before many days' time.

In two days' walk, he came near Xetsi's camp.

There was no darkness now, only a twilight through the narrowest part of the night, and he knew he could not approach under cover of their sleeping.

So he crept within view of the bay where the family set their nets, at a place close to the camp but well hidden, to watch until the chance came.

He hadn't long to wait, he was sure of that. Xetsi and her mother would spend the whole of the day fishing and her father, though unlikely to help, must sooner or later walk along the shore to see how the women were doing.

It was easier than lying breathless in wait for a moose. K'Anta lay in cover from which he could move quickly to the camp when the time came, yet could wait out two or three days if he had to, going to the lake to drink at night.

He watched the two women go down the shore from the camp, his heart quickening. They came close, their voices reaching him. Then they passed into the distance again where they fished and K'Anta watched once more in the direction of the camp.

Her father did not come down the shore that day, but he did early the next morning, shortly after Xetsi and her mother.

K'Anta went quickly to the camp, but watched also down the trail for anyone's return. It was well he did so. Xetsi came toward the camp before he had time to locate the pack of fur.

He withdrew into the nearest cover, lying silent. It seemed an age before she came into the camp, and in that time K'Anta realized with horror that he was too close to get away in silence if the others came before Xetsi left again.

He thought momentarily of speaking to her, then banished the idea. He dared not burden her with what he was about to do.

She moved about the camp in search of something, started to leave, came back again. K'Anta breathed heavily, his face to the ground. I am a fool, I am a fool. Please go, Xetsi.

Then she left and quickly K'Anta came out to where he could see the trail yet search the camp at the same time. Not until he saw the familiar pack where it hung in a tree at one end of the brush shelter did he move. Then, quickly, he took it and was gone.

Chapter 22

K'Anta cached the pack near his parents' camp and returned to the work with his people.

He was anxious now about what he'd done, as anxious as he had been before about Xetsi marrying the Tlingit. He had traded one lot of doubts for another; perhaps even piled one lot on top of the other.

The time dragged and he wished it would hurry. The sooner the trading came and was done, the sooner he might return the furs and face the anger of the man he still hoped would some day be his father-in-law.

He tried for a while to plan beyond the point of returning the furs, but found he couldn't. He had to take that burden off first before he could think beyond it.

His worry eased a little when his father finally broke the camp to begin the trek to the trading grounds. Traveling made good occupation for a head that threatened to burst with the thoughts that whirled about inside it.

When they arrived, most of the others had already assembled. The camp buzzed with excitement.

In disbelief, K'Anta saw the familiar gathering of fresh brush at the place where Xetsi's father always camped. But it was impossible. Perhaps they had sent word they weren't coming, and someone else, possibly one of the older daughters with her husband and family, had decided to camp in their old spot.

Then one of the young men came by where K'Anta stood apprehensively watching the scene, having dropped his trail pack to the ground, sensing the abnormal mood.

"K'Anta. You have just come?"

"I have just come."

"You cannot believe what has happened!"

"Tell me." He said the words in fear, but he would have saved nothing by leaving them unsaid for the tale was the kind which had to be told.

"The mother of Xetsi has accepted the marriage gift of One Without Teeth."

"It is not true!"

"It is true. I will tell you. It is her father really. You know that his pride is in trading. He says she hid his furs because she didn't want to come to the trading ground. They say he planned to marry her to the Tlingit and she wished to avoid it. Maybe, I don't know, it is just what they say."

"I know it is true," K'Anta said, realizing this youth did not know how he had himself been involved.

"Well, that is what it is. His pride is in the trading, you know, and he could not come here without furs. So to punish her, he will marry her to an old man and at the same time he gets furs out of it to trade."

"He is a fool!"

"But it is his business. She shouldn't have hidden the fur. It was a foolish way to act."

"Has the old one taken her yet?"

"No. They will do it after the trading is over. He has to tell the Tlingit he has already married her, but he won't want them to know it is to One Without Teeth. And the old one, you should have seen. He is beyond words, he never expected it to happen. He looks mostly scared. What will he do with a young girl? It is a joke."

Yes, it is a joke and K'Anta you are a fool among fools for it is you who made this joke.

He turned away where his own family had begun to prepare their camp.

He went to a place by the river in the evenings, a little removed from her camp and the others, just as he had at the beaver grounds, in hope of seeing her alone. For two nights she did not seek him there. Perhaps she didn't care to, perhaps she couldn't, for now her mother would watch her more closely than ever. And there was no darkness, barely even a little twilight.

And why should she seek him? She above all others would know who had hidden the fur. It was his fault, and whether she wanted to marry a Tlingit or not, it was better than the punishment meted out to her now.

But she did come the third night, and when she came K'Anta wondered really what there was to say.

She sat near him so they might speak in low whispers, but a little further out from the brush so she might watch her back trail.

"I am sorry, Xetsi."

"You should have known it wouldn't work."

He was quiet a long time while they listened for any sound along the path. Then: "I had to do something. I could not think what else."

"You were there when I came back to the camp alone?"

"Yes."

"It was why he blamed me. I came back alone, then the furs were gone. He wanted to beat me to make me tell where they were hidden, but my mother stopped him. So he has found a better punishment, and he has furs again besides."

"I could not bear you going to the Tlingit."

"Do you bear this better?"

He had no answer.

She went on: "You are a foolish man. It is for the parents to decide what is done with their daughter. They refused you. You should seek another."

"Do you want me to seek another?"

"That is not my business. I am only a woman. A woman is nothing. I belong to my father, and he can beat me if he wants to. He only let my mother stop him because he thought of something worse to do. Anyway, he still thinks I hid the fur and he will get it back after I get used to being that ugly one's wife. That is why I came here tonight, to ask you, where is the fur?"

"It is cached. I will bring it. It will take me a few days. I will be back by the time the trading is finished. But do not tell him yet

133

I took it. I will tell him myself. Not unless he is going to beat you to tell where it is."

"I will not tell, even if he beats me. What does it matter? A woman is nothing. When One Without Teeth finds he is too old, he also will beat me. Already my mother has warned me against it."

The murmur of the river drifted up to them, interrupted by the occasional sound in the camp, and K'Anta searched for courage to ask what he had never dared ask before, what, in fact, there had never been a chance to ask.

Finally: "Xetsi?"

"Yes."

"You know why I have made all this trouble."

"Yes."

"If it was yours to say, is it me, K'Anta, you would want for your husband?"

She turned to look at him. "It does not matter. I have told you, a woman is nothing. You see how the hunters beat their women. What can it matter? It is not a question a man asks of a woman."

K'Anta met her eyes, more deliberately than ever before. "I would never beat you. And I have asked you this question."

She rose to her feet, facing the river. He rose, too, standing behind her.

Quietly, but still so he could hear, she replied: "If it was mine to say, I have always wanted K'Anta for my husband."

And she turned, running, back to her camp.

Chapter 23

K'Anta went for the fur, traveling steadily, resting only a short while in the heat of the afternoons. The constant traveling gave some respite from the rage of emotions and a chance to try to sort out the lesson of his failure.

Yes, the trading ground was where Xetsi's father had found his pride. As a trader, he could call himself a man, never mind what others thought, just as K'Anta, as a hunter, knew himself, for himself, to be a man.

You cannot take away the means of a man's believing in himself. So the old fool had to come to the trading ground just as he had had to come to the trading ground every year since the trading had come to be his pride—even at the price of his hope to marry Xetsi to the Tlingit.

But what about old One Without Teeth? Surely he did not ever expect anyone to accept his ritual offer. Surely it had become its own end, this pantomime of manhood, carried on only in the security that it would never be taken as real. But what could he do now? Even such an absurd object of pity as One Without Teeth must have his pride. Surely he was trapped, just as they all were trapped in this entangling snare of the pride of some and the love of others. And even in the love, was there not pride?

And K'Anta wrestled as the young must do with the puzzles of life, dimly perceiving, finding certainties only to lose them, and making a course of action not from the sureties of reason but from the wellsprings of half-seen emotion.

When he returned, he cached the pack a short distance from the camp, then went in to see what had happened in the trading.

The last bargaining was under way. Most of the trading was

completed, and only the younger hunters still had fur with which to feel their way into the process of offer and refuse, harangue or treat with silence, reject but finally accept.

There was time for it, so K'Anta went to his father's shelter to sleep. The exhaustion of the trail added to the weariness of his anxieties left him little zest for what he now must try to accomplish. Yet try it he must, there on the unfamiliar ground of the trading place, for he had no other way that he could see.

By the next midday, the trading was over. The last of the fur had been offered and bought. Though it had been paid for more generously than before, it still had not been paid for in so much as one gun.

K'Anta chose this time, as both the Tlingit and the people began gathering their outfits in preparation for leaving.

He brought the pack of fur unnoticed into his father's shelter. There he broke into it, putting aside a third part, mainly the best of the marten skins.

The rest he took out into the place between the two rows of shelters, those of the Tlingit on the one side and of the people on the other, where the trading was done.

There he laid them out, the furs he had caught for Xetsi's father during the time he had done bride service in growing confidence that he would marry Xetsi.

No one noticed at first for, since the trading was over, everyone was preparing to leave.

Then one Tlingit saw him, standing half-turned away from the furs on the ground.

This one spoke out in surprise. Others turned to look.

Then the word spread to the other side and the people came from their shelters to witness a strange event, a young hunter choosing to act outside the customs of the trade place, to withhold his fur until the time for trade was past.

K'Anta grew conscious of the circle of eyes, those of the Tlingit as well as of the people, which watched him. But he did not move from the position he had taken, half-turned away from the offering of fur.

For a long time, no one came forward from the Tlingit side.

136

K'Anta had expected this. Even the Tlingit might hesitate to respond when something is done out of proper time. But K'Anta held his position.

Then a Tlingit came forward, not a young Tlingit of K'Anta's age but an older man, one who might reasonably step forward in an exceptional circumstance.

He looked a long time at the fur, then went to his shelter, bringing back a knife which he placed on the ground.

K'Anta saw, but made no move to accept.

Neither did the Tlingit speak, and that much at least was set: this bargaining would be without the shouting and waving of arms that some enjoyed, others disdained.

K'Anta met the eyes of the Tlingit, then looked down to the furs and the knife, then looked away.

The older man waited and K'Anta knew why he waited. He waited to let K'Anta know that this was the price, this was all he would get, and that young hunters do not bargain with grown men, they take what they are offered.

But K'Anta was a grown man, too, even if the growth had been recent and painful.

He, too, waited.

He waited, believing one thing: that the Tlingit would not go the long journey back knowing there was fur they had not secured, which might be the weight in their packs rather than the trade items they had already carried in over the long trail.

He strongly suspected another thing: that the people were far from knowing what the Tlingit really would pay to avoid leaving fur behind and carrying trade items back to the coast.

He desperately hoped a third thing: that in reality the fur brought far more on the coast than the people had ever been told, that the trade goods were far cheaper than the people even imagined, and that the greed of the Tlingit, if put to the extreme, had yet to be measured.

And so K'Anta waited.

After another long time, the Tlingit fetched another knife but when K'Anta saw from the corner of his eye that this was all, he did not so much as look down when it was placed beside the fur.

A murmur went up from the circle of eyes, then died away.

The Tlingit spoke, but K'Anta did not understand the words, only the anger. He turned to look into the eyes of the Tlingit and, doing so, he wondered how long the Tlingit might restrain his anger.

The old people spoke of the danger of anger at the trade place and how it could lead to fighting. And they feared anger, for they feared fighting with the Tlingit whom they suspected always had the guns secretly with them, cached along the trail, perhaps one or two even in their shelters.

K'Anta feared this, as he had feared other things. He had feared the blundering approach of the bull moose impassioned in the rut, too, but he had stood his ground before it, waiting until the right moment to release the arrow.

So having met the eyes of the Tlingit for a long while, he looked away again.

The Tlingit went back to his shelter and K'Anta could watch him without turning. He began ostentatiously to go on with his preparations for leaving.

For a very long time, perhaps almost half the time from the middle of the day to the time of the evening fires, K'Anta stood alone then between the rows of camps, and as the Tlingit had gone back to their preparations to leave, so also did the people.

K'Anta knew their thoughts. Look at him. It is what he deserves, if he will be so foolish. There is a proper way, and he scorns it. These were the thoughts of the people and they might be right, K'Anta thought.

But still he waited and in all that time he did not visibly move, though secretly he tensed and relaxed his muscles in turn to fight the fatigue of being motionless, just as he did when he waited for a moose to break from cover.

Then the Tlingit returned and this time he added two nesting cooking pots to his offer.

Now K'Anta moved. He squatted down and, reaching over the furs, he put the two pots and the two knives into a compact pile, moving them away from the furs as he did so. Then he stood up and held his hands before him, the palms toward the Tlingit.

The Tlingit understood for he cursed K'Anta in words K'Anta did not need to know to measure their anger. He only wondered again how much anger the Tlingit could feel and still restrain it for if K'Anta's persistence in the trading led to fighting, he would bring disaster to his people.

But he must risk it, for the object of his trade was Xetsi.

The Tlingit gathered the trade items and took them away.

Again, K'Anta stood alone but this time with only the furs before him.

And this time, he stood alone long into the night, long after the evening fires were lit, long after he had come to believe he might have failed and that his certainty that the Tlingit could not bear to leave furs behind was no more certain than his earlier conviction that taking the furs would keep Xetsi's father from the trade place.

The twilight which took the place of darkness passed and the sun rose again.

K'Anta still stood as he had through all the previous afternoon, offering his furs to trade.

But the camps only pretended to sleep. They lay awake and watched, both the camps of the Tlingit and the camps of the people and K'Anta knew they watched. Because they watched, he did not rest.

Morning fires were built into a bright warming blaze from the remaining coals of the evening fires, and K'Anta longed to stand before his father's fire, to warm away the stiffness of his muscles and the chill of the hours when the sun was down. But he could not.

Then the Tlingit came again to K'Anta, standing before him.

K'Anta met his eyes.

The Tlingit spoke one word and it was the same word in both their languages.

"Gun?"

K'Anta nodded.

A buzz of murmured talk went up from the people when the gun appeared, but the Tlingit camp remained silent.

The Tlingit laid the gun before the furs, along with two bags. These must be the fire powder and the bullets.

K'Anta met the eyes of the Tlingit again, nodded his head again.

The Tlingit squatted, pushing the fur away, then laying his hands over the gun.

K'Anta understood. It is the pride of the Tlingit that he must win in the trade, and even if he has lost in the trade, he must seem to have won—though K'Anta doubted now that the Tlingit ever lost in the trade. Here, in this gun, was surely the proof of that.

But K'Anta had expected this. He fetched the furs he had left in his father's shelter, the fine marten skins and these he laid beside the others, slowly, so the quality of each might be seen.

This time, the Tlingit nodded his assent.

The Tlingit took the fur and K'Anta the gun, the bullets and the powder.

Chapter 24

The gun in his hand excited K'Anta, but he forbade himself to look down at it. He kept his eyes ahead through the camps to the shelter of the brother of One Without Teeth.

The people watched him and he burned with their watching. He had preferred their turning away when he had chosen to go against the proper ways of the trade than their envy now that his nerve had won him the gun.

And he suffered the affliction the people had caught from the Tlingit, the affliction of the pride of wealth. The gun was wealth, beyond any the people had known.

But if the Tlingit lived by this affliction, the people knew its dangers, for it contradicted the sharing essential to their survival.

So K'Anta did not look again at the gun, and he tried not to feel the weight of it in his hand.

He found the man he sought, old One Without Teeth.

He stood before him, only to realize he could not frame into words the proposition he wished to make.

So he held out the gun for the other to take, preparing to wait again for the offer to be understood.

The aged eyes in the sunken face with the grotesque and vacant mouth fixed on the gun, then flicked between the gun and the youth who offered it.

Silently, K'Anta begged him to understand that here was the means of pride, the way out of the predicament of Xetsi's father's accepting his marriage offer, of giving up the marriage that had come too late for him to use. Here was the way for him to give up the marriage, showing before all the people that he had done it by choice.

Then old One Without Teeth might yet think well of himself, and if he thought well of himself, it would not matter what others thought. Pride is a lonely thing between a man and his inmost solitude.

One Without Teeth accepted the gun, fondling it in his hands as a child might a toy.

Chapter 25

The camps broke up quickly. The brother of One Without Teeth arranged with the Tlingit to show them how to use the gun, but they stayed for the lesson after the others had left for fear they might find it beyond them.

K'Anta did not go to Xetsi's camp before he left with his father. Now that he had shorn from everyone the last doubt as to who possessed Xetsi, he would not hint in the presence of the other camps at the urgency with which he wanted her.

Instead he stayed in his father's camp through the salmon fishing, until they moved into the fall hunting camp.

Then he gathered his light trail pack, took his weapons and casually left.

He found the camp where he had expected, in the place out of which he had hunted the season before.

Her mother looked away as he entered the camp and he felt his own approval of her avoidance.

It was Xetsi who spoke: "You must be tired. You have come a long journey."

And she made him a place at the fire across from her father, who now acknowledged him with a diffidence that waited upon K'Anta to make or leave alone the little talk that might be appropriate between a man and his son-in-law.

Then she brought him food, apologizing at the same time for its quality. "We have only the salmon. We have not been lucky in the hunting."

"Never mind," K'Anta replied. "I will hunt tomorrow and soon there will be meat." And he knew that they couldn't be lucky in the hunting, for without himself who did they have to hunt? The pride of the hunter burned warmly inside him.

Then Xetsi brought new moccasins, taking off his old ones, putting on the new. They were exquisitely decorated, and K'Anta knew without looking that every cut and every stitch would be perfect.

His mother-in-law also made a gift, a decorated hunting bag, and he accepted it as she gave it, knowing that it came to him in gratitude that he was her son-in-law—just as any mother returns the generosity of the marriage gift with gifts of acceptance to the man who now owes her more than he owes his own parents.

Later, Xetsi took him to the shelter apart that she must have fashioned for them even while she waited for his coming.

It was small, this shelter, only so wide as to provide a thick mattress of spruce bough tips laid over with robes, beside a small fire. But it was all the shelter they needed, for it was the shelter against the loneliness and the hunger of the heart, the shelter where the comforts against the harshness of the life of a hunting people would be treasured for a lifetime between them.

So, timidly, in her shyness and his anxious tenderness, they began to discover each other.

Chapter 26

The resonance of Dave's voice had occupied the tent for so long that its absence left it vacant. As though to fill a void, I noisily heaped the fire with wood, letting the draught roar into the open door of the stove for a long while before I closed it. The light of the fire danced anew on the canvas of the teepee, and we drew ourselves into the present out of the darkness in which Dave's story had unfolded, since the burning out of the candle many hours before.

"The people do well to remember him." My own voice sounded strange, intruding and of little consequence, mouthing a triviality.

"Yeh. Mostly they 'member him I guess 'cause he breaks the price on that trade goods. Them Tlingit still don't bring guns after that. Still the people don't have guns for long time, pretty near till they find the gold in the Klondike. But after that time that one man he breaks him down, he holds out on his fur like that 'n he don't let that Tlingit beat him, after that you can buy lots stuff with fur. Maybe one marten skin, you can buy shirt 'n two marten skin you buy wool pants."

And, with the story quite finished, we lay as we had all through the long evening, on top of our sleeping robes in the heat of the stove.

I slept poorly, late though it was, the story coming back to me mixed in dreams of the unsettling sort which lie halfway between wakefulness and sleep.

The world of our own journey upon that long and ancient river did not become fully real again until a little before dawn when I fired the stove once more and put on the billy of water for tea, foraging around at the same time in the grub bags for the hefty

145

slab of bacon. We were going to break the camp that morning, despite our shortage of sleep, but not early—and then, as it happened, not at all.

The full light of another wind-blown fall morning was on us by the time the dishes were washed and the interior of the tent was in some order for packing up. We both stepped outside for a first taste of the day, I to dump the dishwater and Dave to do his habitual scan with his old but still sharp eyes of the stretch of river before us and the slopes of the hills behind the camp.

I stood beside him with the empty pan and joined his search. But I did it consciously, not in the inborn way of my old companion whose eyes simply went on in the search for game, whatever else the rest of him might be doing.

"Bear!"

I have forgotten who said it, but the saying of it only reflected the quickening of us both in the recognition of the distant spot of brown that moved in the ambling gait of the grizzly along the upper slope of the northern hill, moving, fortuitously, with the wind, from west to east.

Then the reckoning.

"It's a long way to go, Dave."

"Yeh. But he not move fast. You can make it. You go fast and you climb draw where he's maybe go in. Maybe you get one long shot. He's all you need with you big rifle."

And I used just that little time I needed to fetch the binoculars and confirm what we both believed but hadn't bothered to say: that here went a magnificent grizzly, huge and richly furred in brown with the silvery oversheen that was the much-sought classic in grizzly pelts. That hide would cover the greater part of my living room floor and if I should lift a corner and shake it, the glistening fur would ripple as if it were alive. My children could lie on it on a winter's night with a book and relish the warmth and the softness and the feel of it to the touch.

To me it was that hide, that beautiful, rippling silver-tipped hide. To Dave it was just that when you have the chance you kill a bear.

You kill a bear, for though you cannot eat him you have spent

146

your life constantly half-anxious about what he's going to do next. You leave a camp untended, and he tears it up; you cache some meat and you don't return in time, and he's dragged it off to bury it somewhere. But worst of all, you never know when he will attack you.

For he is the one animal, this grizzly bear, who does not always turn away from man. You may encounter him anywhere—in your camp, at your fishing place, inadvertently at his own kill—and he may attack.

Not one Indian hunter does not know of someone who lost his life in such a way, and there is, if you need any more persuading, that old man by Klukshu who does not have his mind now because he was mauled and left for dead, but somehow survived.

You kill a bear.

And Dave now had said, you can make it. You go fast. Maybe you get one long shot. He's all you need with your big rifle.

When last I saw the bear before I entered the timber he had stopped his ambling for a long while, and I was encouraged that indeed I might well make it.

I traveled fast then, eating up the yardage through the valley bottom that would bring me to the foot of the slope at the mouth of the draw, which I would use for cover in the climb.

I exercised no caution. I made noise and I winded myself willingly; for it was later on, when I reached the top third of that hillside, that I would need stealth and a steady hand.

The mouth of the draw was not as evident in the timber as it had seemed it would be when I had looked at its upper reaches from a distance. I wasted little time scouting and started climbing. Soon the contour of the hillside gave me clues, and I found the cover I wanted. It was a good draw for traveling, and I pressed myself, calling on will power when muscle and lungs began to tire.

After I had climbed enough to have a sense of having made better than half the slope, I worked out to westward, into the wind. I came into the open but could see nothing of the bear. I turned my binoculars then onto the camp. Dave, across the distance that dwarfed him beside the tent, made an upward motion with his hand, knowing I would see it in the glasses.

I went back into cover and climbed some more, but now I climbed slowly, recovering breath as I went and avoiding noise by choosing my footing with care.

It was by no design that I finally met him. I had come out of cover again, cautiously I thought, to scout the slope to westward and above me.

And suddenly, without me in cover, without my having crept cautiously into view, he was there, immense and silent and staring without expression directly at me from something less than thirty yards—and I was locked into a mutual awareness with that beast from which there was no going back to begin again, to do things properly.

I slid the safety off and raised the rifle.

In the scope the massive head—punctuated with snout, small eyes, and ears—lay without relief against an even more massive backdrop of shoulders blending into chest and girth and powerful forelegs.

Now I could shoot, though I did not like the shot. The small brain in that massive head was a difficult target; around the head there was too little showing of the chest and shoulders.

If he would just turn sideways I could take him in the shoulder where, inside a generous eighteen-inch circle, lay spinal column, shoulder blades, heart, lungs, even the upper portions of the forelegs. A bullet striking any of these would bring him down and expose him for a second rapid shot, even a third.

He did not turn, not just then.

Then, consciously and deliberately, somewhere short of that first rise of panic that accompanies danger even in men who do not, finally, ever panic, I dealt with the fact that if he charged, this shot, which I did not like now, would be enormously more difficult; and it would be forced upon me within the moments before he reached me.

I dealt with it and did not shoot.

I do not know how long we waited, the bear and I, for something else to happen.

But I could not wait indefinitely, for I had the rifle trained upon him for a standing shot, and as the moments went by so did the chance of my making that shot good if I had to. The muscles in my arm and shoulder could not balance that rifle much longer, but I did not care to take it down and then have to put it up again against his charge.

So I changed position, down to the standard kneeling shot, and from there I could wait as long as I wished.

And then he moved, and momentarily—as I would have treated any movement from him after that damnable wait—I took it that he was coming.

But he wasn't. He swung his great forefront up the slope and, thrusting with his hind legs, began to leave. In that second, and for a few more as he made for cover, he left me the shot I had waited for—the shot that would put that glistening hide on the floor of my living room, the shot that Dave, far away at camp, was waiting with certainty to hear.

I did not shoot.

And the bear was gone.

And with the departure of the bear came the problem of what I would tell Dave; even I did not know why I had not shot except that it had something to do with whether I had any right to shoot except to eat, and even that seemed so damned silly to me after the event that I wouldn't offer it to myself, much less to Dave.

But there must be something to say in such a circumstance, I thought. But of course there wasn't, and there was even less by the time I came, apprehensively, back into camp. There Dave, with what feelings I had no way of knowing yet agonized to know, said not a word.

So I said: "I didn't shoot," and left it at that.

And the day passed rather uneventfully with our agreeing first that it was too late to start out and we should make an early go of it the next morning, then tending a bit of gear and catching a little sleep and walking out once for grouse with, oddly, no luck.

But the magic that had built up during the previous days and culminated in the final night of storytelling—and through which I had felt myself so nearly allowed in to that world made of whatever really mattered to Dave—was gone.

Nothing I could do, certainly, could capture it again.

Chapter 27

So finally, the next morning, after five days and nights, we put ourselves back on proper river schedule. We had the outfit rolled and stacked by the canoe as the first strong light showed a low, dense mist hanging over the water.

"Maybe sunshine today."

"Yes," I agreed, "fog on the water, maybe sunshine when it lifts."

We packed the canoe then shoved off. Soon the current had caught us and the paddles were dipping, long casual strokes, the drops running off the blades between strokes and spattering a moving line of rings on the water.

The overcast had cleared and when the fog lifted the sun shone, though with little warmth.

The long curves of the river slid steadily by. We cut through two shallow sloughs, startling a cow moose and calf in one of them, taking a mile off the length of the river each time.

A little after noon we came below Tantalus Butte, bringing the first cabins of Carmacks into view.

I stopped paddling to speak to Dave. "We have to stop by T and D for some candles and a little grub. You want to go any place else?" Carmacks was Dave's home town, if living fifteen miles away on the Whitehorse road and dealing at the trader's there meant that, and I could imagine he might have calls to make, maybe a message to leave for his wife.

"Just by T and D."

We drifted until the highway bridge came into view. The current runs swiftly here and disaster waits for indecision. That spring an old Cree had lost his life when his raft, a difficult rig to direct at best, had been dashed against the most southerly pier.

Three of these piers rise out of the main stream, leaving, for a mid-river passage, two choices: to left or right of the central pier.

There is nothing to choose between either passage; what is critical is that a choice be made. Around the piers the water churns and surges by in a turbulence fit to crush the stoutest canoe or riverboat, and it is indecision that will put you there, nothing else.

But however generous the space between the piers, the shot looks narrow enough when the time for deciding is first upon you, when, from upstream, you look down the gullet of your choosing.

It must have been thus for Dave as well as for me; for, having indicated the right-hand passage, he began to paddle very cautiously, correcting a little leftward, now a little right. His paddle moved often from one gunwale to the other as his estimate of our position responded to the shifts the current forced upon us. As he corrected, so also I paddled in suit.

And then the bridge grew rapidly in size, the roar of the water against the piers filled our ears, the span rushed overhead and we were through.

Nothing to it, really. But I spared a sideways glance at a pier and the power of the water surging around it and thought of the old Cree.

But Dave thought of our landing at the trader's and set us for it. Within minutes we were ashore with the canoe securely tied.

It was a small store, its limited space given over to packed shelves on every side and a counter for the writing down and the passing back and forth of money. In the middle of it all stood a huge stove that would be stoked to a fearful heat in the cold of winter.

And all about, that strange mixture of wares that now penetrates the north: traps and snare wire, hair shampoo and curlers; firearms and ammunition, paper plates and plastic picnic forks; duffle cloth and felt boots, plastic children's shoes and disposable diapers; flour and beans, TV dinners and instant mashed potatoes. Half of it was vital, and you could have thrown the rest in the river for all anyone needed it.

We sought our own needs. A dozen candles—we'd burned more than our ration at Little Salmon—more of the ubiquitous tinned bully beef, more tea, some sugar, to allow for the amounts with which Dave laced his brew, and more maple syrup, for hotcakes and bacon, flooded in maple syrup, had become the standing breakfast.

Dave borrowed paper and pencil and slowly made a note for his wife, the kind of note, I'm sure, I'd often had from him when stopping by his camp.

"I cant wate I got to go down to get beaver at river trale get to soft for snosho after noontime you take 2 lynx 1 foxe to Bay in Whitehors my wife givs you and you sent mony to post office, your frend Dave," it would say, and I would sell the pelts to the Hudson's Bay then send the money to Dave through the Post Office. Then he'd have a little cash which the trader who'd given him credit for the winter's trapping wouldn't know about or, suspecting, would be incensed by. Dave could spend the money at the other store for some luxury his extended credit at the trader's would no longer stand and a little beer at the hotel besides. To top it off, he'd feel half-pleased and half-guilty and would trap all the harder to make up for it with the next fur he took where his credit had come from.

I treasured Dave's notes, and I waited while he built the one for his wife, one word carefully after another, in the fashion the missionary had taught him long ago.

Then he handed the folded paper to the storekeeper. "My wife comes to store, you give her." The note went in a slot where many come and go in an informal post over the year, and if Dave's wife caught the Dawson-bound bus some morning on the highway by their camp to ride the fifteen miles to Carmacks, she'd have a message waiting at the store.

Our stop at Carmacks did also for lunch, made without tea and fancied up with store cookies, and then hurriedly finished, for there was little good camping above Five Finger Rapids and we didn't care to be in the rapids too late.

Back on the river, we paddled in earnest, one curve then another passing by until the sound of the rapids rose above the immediate whispering of silt against the canoe skin.

The Five Finger Rapids is just that: a narrow canyon in the Yukon where the converging current is divided by four pillar-like islands into five white rushing fingers of rapid water, spewing through, forced by the whole volume of the river backing up behind it.

Here the great paddle-wheelers churning upstream passed out a line to be taken laboriously up the bank and secured above the rapids. Once it had been secured ashore to a tree or a ring bolt set in the rock, it would be reeled in on the steam-driven capstan, aiding the broad paddles as the steam pressure strained on the safety valves, and the boat inched through against the current.

With a quickening pulse and a sense of commitment, you round the last bend to see the pillars of rock rising formidably before you tearing the stream apart. You have one last chance now to turn away: you may paddle like hell for the right bank and go in.

But if you were the kind who turns away at last moments you wouldn't be here: so your heart rises, your muscles tense, your scalp tightens, and you prepare to go through.

I wondered a moment about Dave's thoughts. Perhaps he thought of me. In any event, for the first time in that journey he shifted sideways in the canoe to look back.

He smiled a wide smile and made a swooping motion with his hand. It indicated how we would be swept through by the current of the far right channel.

I returned the smile and pointed my paddle skyward, shaking it vigorously to signify my defiance of the river.

"Keep to middle!" he shouted then and, still with the smile, turned back to the job.

We approached a little to the left of center and the current quickened. We paddled hard to correct to center, then found the current moving us over as well.

Suddenly the swiftness took us. One second we had been approaching, the next, with alarming sureness, we were taken.

The roar swelled into a crescendo, a blanket of noise descending over everything, immersing us.

153

The water raced away into the chute and we went with it. The canoe rose onto the long tongue of slick surface that shot between the rocks and was hurled down its length.

I glimpsed the towering wall of rock to the left, then lost track of everything as the canoe pitched violently in the combers at the end of the tongue. I drove the paddle in fright and determination as a gallon of water came inboard on the left.

Dave had held his paddling. Then suddenly, as the next set of rolling combers rushed up at us, we both thrust the paddles with all we had for the quiet water to the right. The canoe pitched again, less violently, but responded to the paddles and we skirted, barely, the remaining rough water.

As suddenly as we had gone in, we were out.

We slipped along by the right bank, using the fast water, and soon made a channel by an island above the mouth of Tatchun Creek.

"You want to camp here?" The sound of the rapids had fallen astern and Dave could speak to the side, easily heard. It would be the last good site before the flats near Yukon Crossing. Still, it was early.

"Can we make Yukon Crossing?"

"Oh, yeh, we make Yukon Crossing."

So we paddled on and just at dusk, Dave motioned to the bank a mile above the crossing where the river swings away from a cutbank on the right, leaving a flat shelf at river level. Here, in a stand of mature spruce, we came on a perfect clearing for the teepee, not fifty feet from the landing, with plenty of dry wood in nearby clumps of willow and aspen.

Late though it was, I made fresh bannock by the candlelight and we sipped tea while it cooked. Then we slathered tinned butter on hot slices of it, turned out a steaming pot of beef chunks in gravy over it, on our plates, and finished up with more bannock and butter and bitter marmalade and the final billy of tea.

"We travel with you, we gonna get fat," Dave declared, sugaring up his tea and reaching for another knife blade of butter.

"We don't go on the river to suffer, Dave. We go on the river to enjoy life."

154

Dave grunted an acknowledgment of the wisdom in that phi-losophy, then added: "Tonight, I goin' to tell you 'bout some fellas, whitemen, I take out one winter from Yukon Crossing. Real green-horns, real cheechako. They damn near get me in trouble."

And I wondered if somewhere, perhaps in the midst of the rap-ids, I had been forgiven for the business about the bear. I had no way of being sure, but I took comfort again in the magic of the storytelling.

Chapter 28

It was years ago that it all took place, during the first war, he thought. He had been married only a short time. He and his wife had been at Yukon Crossing where he had cut some wood for the roadhouse on the winter trail. He was ready to go back to Little Salmon, but had had to wait for enough snow to use a toboggan. He'd come down earlier on a raft and had brought his winter outfit, including his dogs, knowing he would not return until freeze-up.

His work had paid well. He had a new tent and some whiteman's grub he'd bought from the roadhouse, and more shells for his Winchester. Besides this, he had a few dollars to take back to Little Salmon to pay some of his debt and renew his credit for the trapping season.

At Little Salmon his wife had left much dried salmon in a cache, which would last most of the winter. They would hunt moose on the way home, and, all in all, it looked like a prosperous season.

The whitemen arrived on the northbound winter stage, not long after the river froze over. They got off with a huge pile of outfit, carrying it with much fuss from beside the sleigh to the roadhouse kitchen, while the driver put the horses away for the night. From his tent set nearby, Dave watched but paid little attention, except that he noticed the taller of the two seemed to have charge of the other, giving directions all the while about what to carry in next and where to put it.

Later that evening, this same one came and said loudly outside the tent that he wanted to talk to Dave.

Dave pulled on his parka and slipped out through the door flap.

156

"You the Indian they call Dave, the fella in the roadhouse told me about?"

Dave grunted his assent.

"Okay. Well listen here, now. I gotta go up the Yukon River from here, and I'm gonna hire you to take me up with your dogs, me and my partner."

Dave hesitated, uncertain how to reply. He didn't want to take anyone up the river except himself and his wife, but this man had already said he was going to hire him. He wasn't sure how to say he didn't want to take him, and before he got that figured out the other was talking again.

"We're going up the Yukon a ways, then we'll have to go up another river. I'll tell you that when we get there."

"How far up Yukon?"

"Well, I ain't quite sure, but I'll know when I get there."

"Past Little Salmon?"

"Where's Little Salmon?"

Dave was stuck again. The man said he'd know where to turn off when he got there, but how could he know anything about the river if he didn't know where Little Salmon was.

"Little Salmon is next place after Carmacks."

"Yes. Well, that's fine. I got a map a fella gave me that shows me where I want to go. If Little Salmon is next after Carmacks, we'll be going past there. Anyhow, I'll follow the map as we go along, and I'll know where to cut off."

Dave felt trapped. It seemed established that he was going, so much so he couldn't actually refuse now, and he wasn't sure how things had got that far in spite of him.

He tried something else. "Pretty tough to go up river now. Maybe you camp here now, you go on first boat going upriver next spring."

"No. I gotta go up there now. You get your rig all ready to go. I don't want to waste time hangin' around here. I already wasted too much time in Whitehorse waitin' for the stage to leave. Now, I'm payin' you a hundred dollars a month for you and your dogs, and there's no pay till we get outa here. So you better get your rig fixed up to move, whatever you have to do."

157

With that he left, turning only to say as an afterthought that he, Dave, could call him Harrison, that was his name.

His wife had heard every word through the light canvas of the tent, and he knew in their silence that neither of them liked what he'd gotten into, but neither did they know quite how or why nor what could be done now. Dave was inexperienced with whitemen. What he'd been offered in wages was half the going rate, but he hadn't the least idea how to ask for more.

In the morning he went to look at their outfit, resigned to the arrangement. It sat in a heap in a large room at the roadhouse used for eating. Harrison rummaged in one of the dunnage bags. Another man stood off and Dave recognized him as the second of the two he'd seen come off the stage.

"This's my partner. You can call him Bill. You ready to go?" Harrison finished with the dunnage, dropping it back on the heap.

It was an impressive heap of outfit, depending on what you figured to do with it. As far as piling it all on a toboggan went, it was out of the question.

Also, it was mostly new. The sleeping bags were new, the dunnage bags were new, an immense, heavy tent was new and everywhere about were boxes of Heaven knows what. A handsome Winchester rifle stuck out of the pile.

"You got too much outfit," Dave finally managed to say.

"What the hell do you mean, too much outfit? We're gonna be out there all winter."

"Can't put that much on sleigh 'n my dogs can't pull it." He'd learned not to hesitate, for surely if he did, Harrison would have him cornered again.

"Well, by hell, we'll get some more dogs and another sleigh, then. I'll drive a dog team, too. You go round up some dogs. I'll pay for 'em."

The nearest place to buy dogs was at Carmacks and then only if the few Indians camped there would give up one or two dogs each.

"No dogs to buy around here. Maybe at Carmacks."

"How far is Carmacks?"

158

"We go one day, come back next day."

"I want to pull outa here today, and I don't want any coming back. I lost enough time as it is. Somebody around here must have some dogs."

The only dogs at Yukon Crossing besides Dave's five belonged to the roadhouse. But they wouldn't be for sale. Dave explained this.

Harrison stared at his pile of outfit, then went abruptly out in search of the operator of the roadhouse.

He returned a little later. "He won't sell me his dogs, damnit, but I got a deal with him. He's gonna rent me the dogs and a toboggan to go as far as Little Salmon. Then we gotta get another bunch there and hire some Indian to bring these back. So let's get the hell outa here, now."

Uneasy, Dave went to work. There would still be trouble. With his own outfit to go back, there was still no taking all of Harrison's. He'd been hoping that the difficulty of getting dogs would kill the whole scheme, but he realized now that Harrison would stubbornly stick to anything once he'd started, no matter how impossible it became.

Dave had seen whitemen like that before, coming and going on the river. He worried now what Harrison was going to do when he told him, as he'd have to, that some of his outfit couldn't go.

Dave and his wife started stripping their own outfit to rock bottom. Everything they could leave, they piled on a piece of spare canvas which Dave then wrapped around it. He would stow the resulting bundle in the gear cache back of the main building.

What remained was sparse: the meagerest cooking outfit; a blanket each for the trip to Little Salmon; a bit of dried meat, and some tea, sugar and flour; dried fish for the dogs, enough to make Little Salmon; spare moose-hide moccasins; her precious box of needles, thread, shredded sinew and homemade awl. With this, he'd take his own tent and the light sheet stove, his own axe and carbine.

Then he went to see about the other dogs and the toboggan. The lodge keeper showed him where the harness hung in the gear cache, and together they unslung the toboggan from the rafters, putting it out on the snow.

"One thing, Dave. You or your wife drive my dogs. Let that guy drive yours if you have to. I don't want any cheechako ruining my dogs."

Dave absorbed that and pushed the toboggan around in front of the roadhouse. Then he went in to confront Harrison again.

"We gonna load your stuff now. But we don't need him all. Your tent, he's pretty heavy. I got light tent. Maybe you got heavy grub, too. We have to see how we make out when we load." And he grabbed the sleeping bags, going out with them before Harrison could start talking.

When he came back Harrison had picked up a box, making to go with it to the toboggan.

"Maybe I load up. Then I know what we got."

"What you figure to do? Paw through all my stuff?" Harrison put the box down.

"We gonna go long time on trail, we got to use little bit right kind of stuff. We take too much heavy grub, we got no room for fish for dogs, we can't go no place. We spend all winter hunting moose to feed dog." It was a difficult speech for Dave. He'd never had to stand up to a whiteman before, and it wasn't easy.

The lodge keeper had come into the room, reading the situation clearly. "Mr. Harrison, you better do what Dave says. He knows what he's talking about. You have to remember you haven't traveled with dogs before, and it's something you have to know about. You hired Dave and you're the boss all right, but still you got to let him decide about the outfit."

"Awright. But let's hurry up about it. I want to get going."

His position strengthened, Dave did now what he'd never have dared on his own. He moved the dunnage bags in which Harrison and his partner had their extra clothing to one side.

"You and your partner don't take all this much clothes. You just take one extra underwear and lots socks, maybe one extra mitts. You got good outfit on now and you got good coat, so that's all you need."

Certainly the trader in Whitehorse had sold them a heap more

160

than they needed, but what he had sold them their lives could depend on.

Harrison threw a bag to his partner and they began dumping out. The lodge keeper moved over to offer supervision which now they were ready to accept and freed Dave to see what was in the boxes.

Some was useful, some wasn't. Dried beans, rice, tea, these they could take. Two boxes of canned meats they couldn't. Half water, they were too heavy for the food they provided.

Three slabs of bacon went on the pile to go, and as much flour and baking powder as he dared allow for bannock. Canned milk was out and with it any hopes Dave might have had that Harrison had any idea what he was going into.

Some lard stayed in for bannock and sugar for tea. A box of dried apricots hung in the balance then went to one side to be broken in half.

Part of the problem lay in Harrison not explaining what he had in mind. If they traveled only on the Yukon they wouldn't need half this stuff. There was a post at Little Salmon and supplies could be had in an emergency at Hootalinqua.

But Harrison wanted to turn up a side river, and from there there was no knowing what would be involved. He was paying by the month so maybe he intended a long trip from the main valley. Would he want to stay long if he found whatever he was looking for? Would he stand for it if Dave had to spend time hunting on the way?

More bags and boxes went into the stay behind pile, followed by a swede saw and a shovel. The rifle went to the lot to go, slowly, while Dave measured the heft and the feel of it. Nice. He'd like to own a rifle like that.

Then an axe and snowshoes.

Harrison had done sorting his dunnage and now sized up Dave's culling.

"What about that shovel? I need that shovel."

"Ground froze now. Can't shovel frozen ground."

Harrison stared at him, about to speak, then stopped. Dave wondered later if that had been the first sign of a break, the first

161

realization on Harrison's part that something was wrong with his plans. But suddenly Harrison turned back to his dunnage and threw it on the pile to go. "Let's not stand around."

Dave finished loading the whitemen's gear, then struck his tent and rolled his own outfit. By midmorning they were ready to go.

Chapter 29

Dave took the trail through Frenchman Lake rather than go by the river. It was early yet, and the river had closed over only a short time before. Though the ice was sound at Yukon Crossing, it would be some days yet before you could trust it in places where the fast current delayed the freezing.

Also, Dave suspected the ice along most of the river had frozen in rough. It had been the sort of fall when ice pans build up and run in the river before the cold comes sharp enough to freeze the stream over at once. Jambs of ice form, and pan ice, much of it forced vertical by pressure, builds up behind the jambs. Thus, stretches of the river would be solid from bank to bank with pan ice frozen in on edge, leaving a ragged surface, hell to dogs and drivers. The verticals wouldn't vary much, but they would be constantly catching at the toboggan or tipping it sideways. An outfit good for fifty miles a day on a clean trail might labor from daybreak to dark and not make fifteen.

And so Dave took the trail up to the benchland, then swung along the river to the southeast where, after skirting a steep cut, he left the river, heading for the valley of Tatchun and Frenchman Lake and the northern approach to Little Salmon.

A dog driver in good running shape, his lungs and heart sound and stout from many weeks on the trail, his legs like springs of sinew, traveling alone with a good team on a good trail eats up mileage the way he eats up hot beans for breakfast, fast and plenty.

The dogs rarely pull his weight, mostly just the toboggan with the loaded outfit: dog food, bedroll, tent, rifle, axe, bit of grub and what have you.

Oh, there's a rush at the start when impatient dogs hit the trail so fast all the driver can do is hang on.

But when the freshness is off, the dogs settle to a steady run that he keeps up himself, his parka on top of the load, his shirt open, even in thirty below. Mileage is what he's after and with the incredible energy of the highly conditioned physique, feeding on moose meat and beans, he lays it out behind him.

But not so with Dave's party. Here was an unmarked trail, with no toboggan track to guide the dogs. Then for each team and driver, there was a spare passenger to ride or run behind.

His wife, lighter than the others, would ordinarily have run part of the time, and ridden when she tired. The men would have spelled around the driving, riding as little as possible, and the day's journey would have been creditable.

But the best they could manage now was as far as a cheechako in poor wind could walk in a day, in rubber boots on unpacked, shallow snow, the kind that slows you down but isn't worth using snowshoes on, especially if you've never used snowshoes before.

So Dave struck out ahead to break trail, followed by his wife driving the roadhouse dogs, followed by Harrison walking behind Dave's dogs, which didn't need driving with someone ahead, followed by Bill in the rear.

Bill was an unknown. He was short and a little blocky, but it was not the blockiness of strength so much as of a softer life. And he rarely spoke, as if his only purpose was to tag along in the shadow of the taller man.

It was Bill who slowed the outfit down. Out of shape and out of wind, without the advantage Harrison had of longer legs, in only a mile or two Dave was conscious of him struggling to keep up.

After a while he couldn't keep up, and Harrison wasted breath cursing him, driving the uneasiness more deeply into Dave's heart. The party on the trail in winter is a small society: it can ill afford hostility and personal abuse.

"Godamnit, Bill, keep up! We've wasted time ever since we left Seattle, and I don't intend to waste any more."

"Doin' my best, Ted. Doin' my best." He puffed the apology out as best he could.

164

Dave cut the pace. The senselessness of Harrison's urgency to rush off to some place he wouldn't disclose so Dave could not be sure how to get there frightened him, but fighting between these strangers frightened him more.

He broke for tea after two hours, then broke again for an early camp while there was still daylight. He could still see the smoke of Yukon Crossing drifting skyward in the clear, cold air downriver, and had he turned his own dogs on the trail then to go back, he could have been there in less than an hour.

He tied the dogs and set his wife to cutting spruce boughs, the two men to packing them in. They had been sweating badly, and he was anxious to keep them moving until the tent was up and the stove lit.

Dave turned to the tent. He cut a dry pine stick, smoothed off the knots, then ran it through the ridge holes at the gable ends of the tent. Then he lashed the pole between two trees and slashed down the next handy sticks for the A-frame at each end to hold the roof out and the short walls up.

Once this was done, he threw in the spruce boughs the others had gathered, then assembled the stove and pipe. By now his wife had gathered dry twigs and the first pieces of wood for the fire. Within moments the tent reached a comfortable seventy degrees above.

Only now did he speak to his cheechakos about what they must do if they were to survive even this moderately cold weather.

"You fellas sweat too much. You goin' sweat too much maybe one week. When we stop for tea or camp you keep movin' around till you can stand by fire or stand in tent. Don't never stand around in cold when you got sweat up. Just so quick you get so cold, somethin' goes wrong, next you freeze. You don't even care you freeze, you get that kind cold."

Dave shoved more wood on the fire, leaving the draught open till the stove turned red, then went on. "You got to dry you clothes. After my wife make grub, me'n my wife goin' clear out and leave you for tent. I put up rope for you so you hang all you underwear and sock and make him dry. You got spare underwear and sock so you change him around all time. Specially, you got to watch out for wet sock in rubber boot. When we get Little Salmon, we goin' get you some high moccasin. Come forty, fifty below, you sweat in rubber boot, you goin' freeze you feet, sure."

While his wife made up a meal of bannock, bacon and beans previously cooked and now quickly heated, and his cheechakos stood by the stove on the other side of the tent, Dave tethered and fed the dogs, gathered an abundance of firewood, then more spruce boughs for the place where he and his wife would sleep by an open fire. As long as it grew no colder, he preferred not to share the tent until, after passing Little Salmon, she would no longer be with them.

Throughout the night Dave slept in spells between which he added wood to his own fire and also the one in the tent. When morning came bacon and beans simmered hot and ready on top of the stove with enough extra to heat for noon and evening. Dave hankered to add dried moose meat, but he'd had bad reactions when he'd offered it to whitemen before and he wasn't chancing it now.

At daybreak they took the trail, falling into the pace which slowly, ever so slowly, would take them to Little Salmon.

The weather held for five days, zero to five above in the day-time, twenty below at night, and at the end of that time they reached the village.

Dave once had done it in a long day on a broken trail.

Chapter 30

Dave took Harrison and his partner to the trading post where the man in charge, a Mr. Simpson, agreed, as Dave had hoped, to put them up in a corner of the fur room. He and his wife joined her people, amidst a torrent of woman talk and noisy dogs as his own and the roadhouse team set up a commotion at the nearness of his father-in-law's huskies.

They had arrived in late afternoon and nothing would have pleased Dave more, after sorting out the dogs and throwing them a ration of frozen fish, than to settle in a favorite corner of his mother-in-law's cabin and pass the long evening with mugs of tea and great chunks of boiled meat eaten off the end of his big knife.

But he did not want Harrison to come barging in in search of him, and suspecting Harrison would do this once he'd had something to eat and his mysterious urgency had come on him again, Dave decided to preclude it by settling everything at once.

So he headed back to the trading post where he found the trader feeding his guests, trying to prise information from Harrison at the same time. The feeding went all right, but the rest drew a blank. Harrison might have been a cheechako on the trail, but he was an old hand at keeping his cards next to his tie clip.

Dave took the chair offered him, then made his opener. "You goin' buy dogs now."

"Sure I'm going to buy dogs, damnit. We settled all that back at Yukon Crossing. You go round up some dogs and bring them here, out front, and I'll buy them." Then to Simpson: "What'll these Indians soak me for dogs? I don't intend to get beaten."

This was too fast for Dave again. Just as he'd been trapped into

167

the trip to start with, he was about to be trapped into something else.

If he had to gather the dogs his position would be impossible. Harrison would beat any Indian in the settlement on the price of dogs, and he couldn't be a party to that. And though he needed to have Harrison buy good dogs, it was only in the interests of the dog owners to sell off their scruff.

Dave could not divide his allegiance. If he acted for Harrison, later he would have to accept responsibility for a team of poor grade dogs, and it was impossible for him to talk to the dog owners about selling good dogs because that was to talk nonsense.

Of course, if Harrison knew the worth of good dogs and were prepared to pay the price, it would have been a different proposition. But Dave knew his man well enough now not to hope for that.

Dave suffered his nervousness, twisting his mitts half to pieces in his hands, but he grabbed control again. "You goin' have to buy you own dogs. Mr. Simpson here he pass word around you want to buy dog, tomorrow people what got dog to sell, he bring him aroun'. Simpson is trader here, so he does business on dog for you."

Harrison glared, then turned to Simpson. "That all right with you?"

Simpson was no fool. He knew who had a spare dog or two and who owed too much credit at the post. As long as he was in the deal no one could keep a little extra cash a secret, and he'd be damn certain that extra cash went right where all cash in an Indian settlement belongs, in the eyes of the trader, right in the old strong-box. "That's fine with me," came his quick reply.

"You got to buy toboggan, too. Mr. Simpson, he helps you buy toboggan an' dog harness. When you get toboggan an' dog harness, I fix 'em up. You goin' buy old stuff anyway, so I got to fix 'em 'fore we use 'em."

"Damnit," Harrison exploded, "I don't want to buy the whole place." But he took another spoonful of beans without waiting for an answer, for it was obvious even to him that he had to have these things.

168

"You got to have moccasin, too, like I say before. But that don't cost you nothin'. My wife makes moccasin for you 'n Bill."

"Okay."

There was a silence. Then, "You mark you foot on paper. I take it back now and my wife, she makes moccasin tonight."

So Simpson fetched some wrapping paper and pencil, for both Harrison and Bill to trace the outline of their feet. This done and the paper passed to him, Dave made his way out into the crisp night air, much relieved.

Simpson followed him to have a word.

"What are these fellows up to, Dave?"

"I do' know, Mr. Simpson. They don't tell me nothin', just only the guy Harrison say he got a map and he got to go upriver. I do' know how far."

"How much they paying you?"

Dave had hoped he wouldn't ask it. He wasn't really sure how much he should be getting, but he knew Harrison had him for far too little and disclosing it would be a measure of both his ignorance and his weakness.

But the question had come as he knew all along it would. "A hundred dollars a month."

"A hundred dollars a month! Damnit, Dave, you can make four times that trapping."

Dave didn't know what to say and Simpson was speechless. There followed a silence in which Simpson grew chilly in the evening air, not having put on a coat just to step out for his words with Dave.

Dave hoped Simpson wouldn't say anything about his credit, and that reminded him of the few dollars in his pocket from the work at Yukon Crossing. He reached for it and passed four well-crumpled ten-dollar bills to Simpson. "I pay you little bit on my bill now. That all I got. But when I done with Harrison, I pay you all I get."

Simpson took the money. "That's all right, Dave. If your wife needs anything while you're gone, she can get whatever she wants."

Simpson turned back toward the door and Dave toward the well-packed path in the snow which led in the moonlight toward the row of cabins along the river bank. Then Dave paused and Simpson, seeing him, stopped also.

"I couldn't help it, I guess, Mr. Simpson."

"I know, Dave. I understand."

There was some comfort in that, but Dave had to put from his mind the thought that whatever he did with whitemen, he always came out looking stupid. He hurried a little in his haste to retreat into his mother-in-law's cabin, crowded with his own people and their easy talk, the intense heat of the overstoked stove, the ever-ready tea and the smells of Indian food, of tanned moose hide and drying fur.

In spite of Harrison's impatience, they did not leave for upriver until the third day. Simpson spent the first day making a compromise on the dogs that met everybody's interests: the dog owners' need not to sell their good dogs; Harrison's or, more accurately, Dave's need to have a half-decent second team on the trail; and, finally, Simpson's need to deal where money on credit extended at the post was wanted most.

The moccasins were ready the same day by noon, but Dave kept them so Harrison and his partner, not knowing enough to knock the snow off when going indoors, wouldn't spoil them by getting them wet.

Also by noon the toboggan had been bought, and Dave spent the afternoon putting it in shape, tightening the cross-members on the bottom boards, reinforcing the handles and repairing the canvas load bag.

The next morning the dogs had been purchased, five in all. Some had collars, some hadn't. Old collars had to be found in the bits of abandoned gear in caches and begged off owners, then repaired and fitted. Dave got the necessary webbing at the post and moose hide from his own supply, making up a harness that would get them by.

That afternoon went in refiguring the outfit. The main need was dog food, and Dave fell back on his own supply of dried fish, plus some frozen fresh fish from his in-laws.

Now that his wife's few belongings were out of his own load, he added a sack of dried meat and more dried beans to both loads.

These again came from the post, and caused Harrison to grumble about all the grub Dave had left behind at Yukon Crossing and now they were buying more, and were they going to spend the whole damn winter eating beans. But Simpson quickly pointed out that dried beans were the sturdiest store food, pound for pound, that a man could take on the trail, and when you considered, failing the luck to kill moose, you might be planning to feed three men for most of the winter, plus two dog teams, on what you could put on two toboggans, it might be as well to see if he could lighten his own load a little to make room for more beans.

Harrison grunted that Dave had already made them leave behind half their clothes, but he quit grumbling about the beans.

Dave wanted to try once more to find out from Harrison how far they'd be on the Yukon past Little Salmon, perhaps even see if Big Salmon was marked on his map. He didn't know whether his chances were best with Simpson present to support him or whether Simpson's presence would make Harrison even more secretive. Failing to decide on this point, he never made the attempt at all.

Simpson undertook to arrange the return to Yukon Crossing of the dogs and toboggan they'd borrowed there, and that being the last unfinished task, early the next morning they pulled out up the river.

Chapter 31

There wasn't the makings of a leader in the dogs Simpson had scrounged up, nor a dog driver in Harrison on short notice either.

But Dave strung them out as best he could and since all he had to do really was get Harrison's team to follow him, it was not so bad an undertaking. He started out with the preposterous expedient of tying a rope from the lead dog in Harrison's team to the left side handle on his own toboggan. There were times at first when his own dogs pulled everything: both toboggans, the other team and Harrison. But after a while the new dogs were less of a problem than the condition of the ice.

The Yukon was a dog-driver's nightmare that winter, just as Dave suspected. A million small pans of ice had formed and piled on edge for miles at a stretch before seizing up in the final freeze.

Even when this happens, there is generally good going along the bars on the inside of the curves. Low at freeze-up, the river exposes these bars, and covered with snow they make for good traveling.

But events in this particular winter had cut these easy stretches to a minimum: the roughing of the river ice was extensive and the river had been higher than normal at freeze-up.

Even where the exposed bar offered good footing, it lasted but a short way before running out against a cutbank. Then tortuous passage had to be made up the river ice and across to the next bar on the other side which, once reached, also quickly gave out.

Dave sought relief from the main river where he could. For a few miles there'd be a side trail he knew, and in other places a slough offered a few yards of decent going. But mainly they had to struggle on the river, dogs scrambling for footing, toboggans bank-

172

ing and bumping, first having to be heaved up and over, then as firmly held back from piling on top of the dogs.

Harrison soon learned how to shove the toboggan about to keep it from jambing against a piece of ice or being dumped, but the effort wore him down. As the day lengthened his temper shortened. Stumbling in fatigue, he wasted more breath in violent cursing.

The nondescript Bill was the best off of all. All he had to keep moving was himself, and the problems of ice, dogs and cheechako driver had the procession down where at last he could stay with it.

Dave camped early and now at least his whitemen were some good to him. They'd learned the routines coming over from Yukon Crossing. In good time the dogs were tethered and fed, the tent was up, the grub was made secure against marauding wolverines, and Dave had a walloping evening meal hot on the stove. In the absence of his wife now, Dave brought his bedroll into the tent, laying the outfit in such a way that all three of them found comfort.

And so they traveled for a number of days, fighting for every yard. Dave reckoned he never made more than ten miles a day in all that journey on the outward trek.

As Harrison hardened into the work and picked up the savvy of the trail he began nagging again at Bill. He expected Bill to help him right the toboggan when it tipped. But if Bill followed close enough to be there when it happened, Harrison would accuse him of walking on his heels. If Bill fell back to get away from that abuse, he'd be cursed out for failing to help when the toboggan tipped.

Bill's pathetic apology became almost the only words he ever spoke. "I'm doin' my best," he would offer, lamely.

"Well, it bloody well isn't good enough!"

And Dave wondered what it all meant and where it could lead. It seemed as though he'd got himself on a trip to nowhere, with the most utter strangers, and it might never end.

At first, Harrison hadn't paid much attention to the river or enquired about the surrounding terrain. But now he began studying the curves and recurves of the stream, the islands and the sweep of

173

the valley. But he seemed to come to no conclusions, and they pressed onward day by day.

Then he began bringing his map out in the daytime when they stopped for tea, or again at night during the short time that a candle could be spared for light to cook by. He guarded it closely, not letting Bill any nearer than Dave. It was a much-folded sheet, perhaps the length of a man's forearm one way, about two stretches of a hand the other.

Dave's anxiety became burdensome. If they kept this up, they were going to land in at Hootalinqua. They'd passed Big Salmon where the mouth of the river and the few cabins deserted a short time ago were clearly visible, but Harrison hadn't seemed to regard these as a landmark in his plans.

So finally one morning after the loads were packed and the dogs harnessed up, just as they made ready to start, Dave spoke up.

"We got to figure out where we're goin'."

"You think I don't know what I'm doing, don't you? Well nobody sees this map but me, and let's get that straight. If you're just angling to see this map, you can quit right now."

Dave began to suspect what lay behind this nonsense now. Crudely drawn maps were as common in the Territory as rabbits in a good rabbit year: maps of creeks in obscure valleys where colors promised nuggets in the grass roots, maps of silver-lead outcroppings high on distant mountain sides, maps, maps and more maps. The only thing coming to be as common a sight now, nearly twenty years after gold rush, were the cheechakos coming into the country possessing one of these, having bought it outside from someone about whom only two things could be certain—first, that he hadn't found treasure in mining values where the map said it ought to be, and second, he hadn't stayed in the Territory to go on looking for it. Otherwise he'd never have had cause to sell the map, if indeed he'd even had cause to draw one.

Dave grunted. "I don't care about you map." He picked up a stick. "I'm goin' to make map now. You look what I show you then you look at you map. We keep goin' like this, pretty soon we come back to Whitehorse where you bought you outfit."

Carefully then, in a clean patch of snow, Dave made a map.

First, he drew the Yukon River from Yukon Crossing clean to Hootalinqua, ending up there with the two streams of the Thirty Mile and the Hootalinqua joining together.

He didn't try to put in every curve and recurve, but concentrated on the main directions and the main shifts in direction on which the river fashions its course.

He studied for a long time what he had done, then traced in the Little Salmon from many miles up to its confluence with the Yukon.

After more concentration, for he suspected this was crucial, he put in the great long sweep of the Big Salmon, from where it rises in the lakes to the east, through its long journey to its mouth, where the deserted village marks the former home of the people who lived on the Big Salmon.

Joining it, he traced in the tributary known as the North Big Salmon.

Then he stopped altogether to watch Harrison's face, and Harrison did not look up from the map in the snow, even after a long time.

With his stick, Dave punched a hole in the snow at the mouth of the Big Salmon. "There is Big Salmon. We pass by already. There was old cabins."

Then he punched another hole. "There is Hootalinqua. We got good going, we be there already. There is Telegraph Cabin and there is White Pass roadhouse for steamboat. Even winter time, some people there."

Again he watched Harrison's face.

Finally Harrison looked up, and for the first time the shove and the arrogance were gone.

"We have to go back to the Big Salmon."

For a long time Dave did not say anything, feeling little more. The ignorance he suspected in Harrison was increasingly confirmed, and yet he never was sure with a whiteman whether there wasn't some mysterious limit to ignorance. It seemed a whiteman could go on doing the stupidest things, yet he would come out ahead, where an Indian acting the same way was sure to fail. It was a feeling he had about whitemen, more than it was something he could point to and say, there, it happened with that one, or that other.

At last he broke the silence. "Anytime you say so, I make map in snow."

Then he turned the dogs and began fighting his way back over the tortuous ice. The others followed.

Chapter 32

They made their way back to Big Salmon in about the same time they had used to come by it. That they were on their own broken trail meant little in the condition of the ice.

With great relief, Dave swung his leader off the Yukon and up the course of the tributary river. The ice conditions there were entirely different, and while an accumulation of soft snow meant a trail had to be broken, at least now he was able to leave his toboggan handles and snowshoe ahead to make the trail. In some stretches the snow was hard and he might have let his dogs run out to make real headway except there was no way for Bill to keep up. So the effort had greatly reduced but the mileage each day didn't really improve.

A short way up the river they camped, then traveled another day and camped again. All the while the candle burned Harrison studied his map. Bill, who had begun to harden in but still felt the strain—he had to wear snowshoes now, even coming last on the new-made trail—sat in unhappy silence on his bedding on the spruce boughs, his feet stretched out to the heat of the stove. Dave cooked, passed grub, cleaned up, then made the second round of tea and pondered about the weather.

The weather had been ideal. The days, still around zero, were just right for men and dogs struggling over a tough trail. Any colder, they'd have to pay more attention to it. Any warmer, they'd be too hot in their heavy clothes. At night the temperature had been ranging to twenty or a little more below, hardly noticeable in a tent with a stove and a pile of wood.

But it couldn't hold. The season grew late. November was

mostly over, and it's a rare November that doesn't bring the first severe plunge of the mercury.

Dave felt the change was in the air. The wind had picked up from the north and a greenish tinge had colored the crystal clearness of the northern sky at twilight. Toward the south and west he could see no haze to hint of weather coming in from a warmer direction.

Even now from the tent, though they were out of the direct strike of the wind, he could hear the sharp swishing of the air rushing through the frozen spruce needles in the tree tops. Later, when he went to bring water to soak beans overnight, he noticed the first dry flakes of a north wind snow.

In the morning they couldn't move. The wind howled out of the north, driving a stinging snow. It was only worth their while to gather more brush for the floor of the tent and some to make shelters for the dogs, then to cut a whopping pile of dry wood, and a little green to mix with it to slow it down.

He had no trouble convincing Harrison and Bill of the need to hold up. Bill suffered visible shock in the face of such a wind and it was hard to keep him out of the tent long enough to have him carry spruce boughs or wood. Harrison on the other hand spent a long time out, finding what such weather was like and what a man could and couldn't do in it. Though Dave still instinctively disliked him, he admired the man's evident basic competence.

It was a fierce blow, and it exhausted itself quickly. On the third day, the wind settled to a four-mile-an-hour northerly drift, and the temperature that night sank to fifty below by Dave's estimate, with every expectation of another ten degrees the following night.

Good men in good condition, with good dogs in top condition, on a fair trail without too much load and with good reason for doing it may travel in such weather, as long as they take it easy.

Dave didn't even consider the possibility, and Harrison's only comment was to ask how long it would last.

"Maybe three, four days. Maybe three, four weeks." He wanted to add maybe all winter but decided against it.

In spite of the cold, Dave began short forays into the nearby timber for moose or a sign of moose, leaving Harrison to cut firewood. The longer the cold spell lasted, the more dog food they used up without making any distance on the river.

The moose sign encouraged him. If he could kill anywhere within a slow one-day foray from camp, he could use the dogs to bring the meat in.

And he much preferred poking around in the bush at fifty below than staying in camp. Harrison cursed his wretched partner more and more now, since Bill seemed to lack the grit even to fetch wood or spruce boughs. Dave grew uneasy as the relationship became more brutal. He felt relieved when he left to hunt in the morning, but anxious as he returned in the evening with the thought that either of them might do something irrational in his absence. Loss or damage to equipment in this climate could mean disaster. Dave wasn't the least complacent for having been born in it.

The temperature settled into forty-five below in the daytime, sixty below at night, as nearly as Dave could say. On the third day after the wind stopped, he killed a dry cow about three miles from camp.

He'd been hunting in a wide circle around the camp, and though he was only that far away at the time he killed, it was late, with little daylight left. In fact, he'd just turned to go back to camp when he'd caught the bit of movement beyond a willow bush, and shifting his own position quickly, he'd shot the cow as she started to run.

Being short on daylight, he quickly took the front legs and shoulders off in one piece on each side, cutting through the hide as well as the meat. Then both the hind legs came off, separating at the hip ball. Pity to cut up the hide, but he hadn't time to skin it out.

The four manageable pieces of meat lay in the snow, where they would rapidly freeze. Then he ran his knife up the line of the belly, spilling the cavity. After that, he gathered brush to throw over the kill in hopes that the brush plus the man smell would be enough to keep off the marauders—the wolves and the coyotes, the fox, the raven and the wolverine—until he could be back in the morning with the dogs.

He made directly for the camp and with dusk thoroughly down he came through the spruce trees that ringed the tent.

He slipped off his snowshoes and was startled as he looked up from the shoe harness to see Bill standing hunched against a tree a short distance off from the tent. He was properly clothed but just to be standing there was foolishness—or worse.

"You better get in tent."

Bill lurched forward unsteadily. Dave knew on the instant the man had been out of the tent for a long time. Fear shot through him. Unused to the cold, the fellow had chilled to exhaustion. It would be like him not to move about but to succumb at once to the temperature, losing altogether what little will he had. The implications swarmed up in Dave's anxious mind.

There was a candle on in the tent and Dave went quickly in. Harrison had the stove going and even a billy of water hot. He sat calmly on his bedroll, barely glancing up as Dave came in, followed by Bill who fell mumbling to his knees by the stove, somehow getting rid of his mitts, then putting his hands to the heat.

"You get anything?" Harrison asked, as though there was nothing strange in Bill's tortured condition.

"A dry cow. Fat." Then to Bill. "Can you feel you feet?"

The reply was unintelligible so Dave came to him and made him sit back on his bedroll. He felt the man's hands. Nothing frozen. Then he undid the moccasins and bared the feet. There, too, Bill had been deeply chilled but not frozen.

"Give me candle," he said to Harrison, who grunted in his usual way and passed the can with the candle stuck on top to Dave.

With one hand Dave held the candle close to Bill's face, with the other he prodded the flesh of the cheeks, the chin, the end of the nose. Bill flinched with pain as Dave's fingers reached for the second time to the left cheek, where he thought he saw swelling.

There was no frost bite. Bill had been struck.

Dave put the candle back and said nothing. Now he would be unable to leave the two of them alone together for however much longer this damnable journey would last.

180

And silently he made the futile wish that they should be Indians or he a whiteman. Dealing with whitemen was difficult at best. But to be alone on the trail, in severe weather, with two whitemen, one at the throat of the other, was the worst predicament he'd ever been in. It might all have been a terrible dream.

He made tea, passing the first hot mugful laced with sugar to Bill, the next to Harrison, saving his own until he had food heating in the pot.

Much later Dave spoke about the morning. He addressed Harrison. "We got to go early for the meat. You got to help me."

"That's fine with me. Just so I don't have to stay around camp with that useless bastard there."

Inside, Dave flinched. Outwardly, he remained unmoved. "We take my dogs and we take axe. Some meat yet we have to chop it up."

Before they left for the meat in the morning, Dave cut wood ahead to last Bill through. Harrison watched but didn't move to help.

Chapter 33

The kill lay unmolested, and the chance to feed themselves and the dogs heavily on fresh meat really threw a bright spot into the gloom.

With the axe Dave chopped the vertebrae and rib cage into manageable sections. Then he went through the frozen mound of innards, salvaging everything useful for the dogs.

After that he and Harrison made up a first toboggan load, taking about a third of the moose.

Then Dave suggested Harrison stay by the kill while he drove back to camp with the load. "No use just to walk back again. You stay here, you watch the meat. You got axe, so you make fire. Before you make fire you put brush on snow for you feet, keep you moccasins dry."

When Dave drove the dog team into camp, he stirred Bill out of the tent to help him. Two men would be needed to rig a stout pole between two trees, then hang the meat with short ropes to the pole.

Dave handed Bill his own axe—he had taken Harrison's axe to the kill—and pointed out the small spruce tree to cut down. It would have been simpler to do it himself, but the time had come when he had to know more about Harrison's partner.

Bill set to willingly but with painful awkwardness. The axe head barely found the tree trunk with each erratic stroke. The blade struck at varying angles and, in the words that crossed Dave's mind, he couldn't hit the same place twice. Soon the tree was scarred and hacked for eighteen inches up and down its narrow trunk, and little closer to being felled.

Dave could ill afford a broken axe handle, and if Bill over-reached just once and caught the handle instead of the blade on the frozen tree, she'd be a goner. But to go now and take away the simple task he'd given him was to say, in effect, here, you're useless, you aren't a man.

Dave shrunk from that. He turned away, pretending to be occupied with the dogs, wondering incredulously how a man could grow up and not know how to use an axe.

Finally, Bill wore his way through the tree and it fell over.

Dave then walked over and said, "I limb him up now and cut him off. You take brush into tent."

And as soon as Dave had limbed the tree Bill awkwardly but eagerly, like a happy boy, gathered the brush and laid it out in the tent, the curve of the branch upward, as best he could, the way he'd seen Dave do it. Then, stumbling in his anxiousness to help, he followed Dave about, lending his awkward hands to every task: holding up the pole against the tree while Dave fixed the props to keep it there; dragging the meat across the snow from the toboggan to the pole; heaving and straining, to little effect, as Dave lifted the meat and made fast the ropes.

The work completed, Dave stoked the fire, making a billy of tea. They sat in silence to drink it. Once when Dave glanced up at Bill's face, the other broke into a sudden smile, childlike, and Dave quickly looked away, not knowing how to respond.

When Dave went back to the kill for the second load he took the billy can and tea makings with him, sharing tea at that end of the now well-packed trail with Harrison. In the clear air swept in from the Arctic, the sun poured brilliantly over the forest and through the trees to the snow below. Although the sun was powerless to raise the temperature to more than forty-five below at best, its comfort to men nonetheless persisted. As nearly as he could hope to, Dave regained some feeling of well-being as he squatted by the fire, his moccasins on the spruce branches, his hands wrapped about the hot mug of tea.

Harrison remained silent, just as Bill had done, but when Dave was drawn to search his face for some answer to the stubbornness and brutality of the man, Harrison stared on into the flames of the campfire, unmoving save to pass the mug of tea now and again to his lips.

They made up the second load. Dave left with this, then quickly returned for the last of it. The trail was now packed and hard, and the dogs were running eagerly in their love of a well-made track. The best of the day was over when Harrison came in with him on the final trip.

The dogs gulped savagely at the fresh meat, ravenous for it after the fish of the last several weeks. Soon they licked up the last red stains in the snow, looking up to see if there might be more.

But Dave wasn't about to gorge them because a temporary abundance had come to the camp. He would feed them well, but a long way from all they'd swallow if they got at the meat themselves.

Like the dogs, the men ate with gusto, too, for after a long time on bacon and beans the chunks of boiled moose meat, still fat from the summer and fall, fed an extra hunger.

Four days later, the weather eased with milder air and snow from the south and they broke camp, heading up the Big Salmon once more. Before leaving, Dave made a pole cache of the meat left after he had packed all he felt was practical on the toboggans.

They made fair time now, for an outfit on the slow side anyway and breaking trail all the way. The storm had brought ten inches more snow, and they were back to zero in the daytime, ten to twenty below at night.

Harrison studied his map every evening now, as long as the candle burned and in the daytime on the trail, too, if Dave paused for any reason. And he watched the landmarks closely, the curves and sweeps of the river, the mouth of every side stream.

Dave would gladly have made another map in the snow, but Harrison did not ask and Dave could not bring himself to offer, even though, as the days went by, he began to fear another overshot, with all the waste of time and precious dog food involved in retracing hard-won distance.

Then one day at noon, far back in the mountains toward the lakes where the Big Salmon rises, in a long stretch of valley where open slopes intersperse with timber and even the river bottom itself affords little protection at times for a camp, or dry wood for a fire, Harrison said they must stop. He would now size up the surrounding country and the next stretch of river by himself.

Dave fixed on the best campsite he could find in the next three or four miles. It afforded enough timber to break the wind, enough firewood to last for ten days without having to haul it a distance with the dogs, enough small spruce for bedding brush and a view from the camp of the south-facing slope to the north of the river.

This latter was important. Dave had grown anxious to kill again. They were now far from Little Salmon, and if they stayed here for long—Harrison had spoken earlier of being out most of the winter —they were going to be short on grub. It was time to shore up against hunger.

There had been no sign of moose for many miles. The valley had changed from good moose ground, and though this wasn't country Dave had traveled often, he doubted there would be improvement for many miles yet.

So he looked to the open slopes for caribou. If he could spot a band of the wide-ranging animals, he would spend a couple of days or longer to kill three or four. Since this idea had taken shape, he'd worried what to do with Harrison, fearing to leave him alone again with Bill. But now Harrison had solved that, declaring his intention to explore the surrounding country on his own. Perhaps all would go well.

The rest of the day went into making a careful camp, including brush huts for the dogs. The depth of spruce boughs in the tent lay three times that of an overnight camp, and the tent itself was set to avoid the wind. With several days' worth of dry wood heaped beside the tent Dave felt secure, so far as the camp went, against any bad change in the weather.

The next morning Harrison prepared to set out, saying that he would need some lunch and that he intended to take his axe.

"I fix you pack," Dave replied, and with a bit of canvas and some rope, made a makeshift sack that Harrison could sling on his back with lunch and axe, and a few dry twigs and a short piece of candle—these last items so he might easily start a fire in an emergency.

One last piece of advice. "If you walk up side creek, some time he is more easy to walk on overflow ice. But you watch out for overflow ice. Sometimes he is not freeze hard yet, you get you moccasin wet."

Harrison left and Dave made another billy of tea then stood outside the tent to sip the tea and scan the slopes for the little movement that would distinguish a caribou from the endless dark clumps of rock and alder that showed through the snow.

He spent the day mainly watching for caribou on the slopes, but now and then attending to some odd task, occasionally fetching in more wood.

With the same fumbling eagerness and responsive smile as before, Bill followed him about to help. Patiently Dave included him in the tasks, though it would have been simpler to leave him in the tent. As the day went on Dave grew aware of an odd warmth of companionship in being alone with this unfortunate cheechako of all cheechakos.

Harrison returned before dark. He unstrapped his snowshoes, hung his pack on the tent frame and, hardly acknowledging the tea Dave handed him, fell to his map again. Dave wondered if the map weren't about to fall apart from folding and unfolding.

Harrison spent the evening in a brooding silence. In the morning, he opened the subject he had so long avoided.

"Make another map in the snow."

Dave cut a stick, then walked out of camp to fresh snow.

First he drew the main stream of the Big Salmon, avoiding the numberless horseshoe bends, concentrating on the proportions of the main directions. Then he laid out as best he could the main side streams.

As Harrison watched, he pointed to his map, describing the mountains to the north and south, telling about the valleys through which his main side streams ran, explaining if they were wooded or open, wide or narrow.

"But," he went on, "there is plenty more side creek. We in country now where there is all kinds side creek. It is hard to make map to show all side creek. This is just main side creeks." Then

186

finally, with a thrust into the snow where he left his stick standing: "This is where we camped."

He looked at Harrison for questions. There were none. He walked away to feed the dogs. Later, looking back, he saw that Harrison had his own map out, studying the two together.

Half an hour later, Harrison hadn't moved. Dave felt a powerful compulsion to go to the man and beg to see the damnable map so once and for all he might tell Harrison whether he could take him where he wanted to go or not.

What unreasonable stubbornness possessed the man to prevent his realizing how ridiculous this all was? To use Dave as his guide on the one hand and hide from him where they were going on the other made no sense. Dave could not fathom it.

He twice stepped toward Harrison with the idea of pledging secrecy, but each time he failed to go through with it.

When Harrison finally left Dave's map and returned to the tent he said he was going out again. Dave gathered him a lunch of bannock and some of the last of the moose meat, putting these in the little pack, while Harrison pulled on extra socks and retied his moccasins.

As Harrison started to walk out of the camp he stopped, looked back to Dave, then returned to talking distance.

Dave met his look directly.

"If a man was looking for a silver-lead outcropping and he knew pretty well exactly where to find it, would he see it in this much snow?"

Of course it had to be something like that, but the directness of the question, giving away so much of what had been guarded with such persistence, took him by surprise. But he didn't let that on.

"You might, you might not. Silver-lead, he sometimes show up on rock face where snow don't hang on. Other times, he show up on slope, sometimes even nearly level ground. But mostly he's on rock face or slope. Mostly, man prospects in summer time."

Dave instantly wished he hadn't said the last bit. It had been simply an observation related to the difficulty of seeing an outcropping in winter weather; it would sound to Harrison like a judgment on all that Harrison had put them to.

But Harrison said nothing further. His face had blackened into a scowl as he had put his question. You couldn't know if his anger had deepened any further. He turned, leaving camp, moving skillfully now, in a long easy stride, with the snowshoes.

Chapter 34

A little after Harrison left, Dave spotted a small band of caribou on the slope to the north of the camp, two to three miles off and halfway up to the skyline of the ridge. Their movement as they foraged for moss beneath the snow gave the animals away.

He rapidly assessed their distance, their direction of movement, the terrain of the whole slope, and the worth of his own dogs.

Then he grabbed his carbine, ammunition, and snowshoes, throwing them on the toboggan, and hurriedly thrust the dogs into harness.

In explanation to Bill: "Caribou on mountain. That way." He sacrificed the second it took to point. "I try to kill some."

Bill trembled at the urgency before him. Then fears rose. "You be back before Harrison?"

Dave found it hard to think about that and buckle dog harness at the same time. "I think I be back before Harrison." Of course he couldn't be sure, because Harrison couldn't be predicted, but it was better to say that and be done with it.

The dogs bolted when they discovered the unloaded toboggan behind them and Dave, as eager as they, rode with one foot on the sled, hitting the snow a frequent shove with the other, clutching fiercely to the careening handles.

He made for a long draw that climbed up the slope for most of a mile and then cut eastward to a point above the caribou roughly in the direction of their travel. He would keep in this with the dogs as long as it afforded cover, probably till he was above the band of caribou, then he would tether the dogs to a clump of brush and make the final approach alone.

The pace fell slack soon after the climb began and the loose snow of the slope gave the dogs poor footing. But urged on, the dogs responded, scrambling upward, snaking the toboggan through the scrub, which grew taller in the draw than on the slopes.

At first Dave pushed whenever he could, scrambling along to keep pace. But when the first mile fell behind and the draw swung eastward, he began saving his own breath for the time when he would go on without the dogs. The pace slowed a bit for this.

The snow on the slope wasn't deep, and even in the draw there was as yet little drifting.

The easterly sweep of the draw steepened more than he had expected, and Dave wasn't sure how far to go. After he estimated a mile from where the turn occurred, he tethered the dogs and crawled out to the southeast crest of his draw to assess his position.

He saw the caribou at once. They had moved further away in the same direction he had traveled. This made use of the draw for cover worthwhile, but it also discouraged him, for if the caribou began moving quickly they could be in the next valley by the time he reached their present position.

He untied the dogs and pushed on, keeping well in the cover of the draw, ignoring the possibility of overreaching, since this was the easiest error of all to correct.

When he tied the dogs again, it took only a moment to crawl to the edge of cover, for he had come to the usable limits of the draw.

The caribou foraged below him now, five or six hundred yards away, beyond the range of his Winchester. But as they foraged, they were moving generally in his direction and there must have been fifty or more. Now he felt the warmth of good hunting. Just ever so carefully now and he could kill three, maybe four. All he must do is wait, not be too anxious.

And the wind was in his favor: slight, what there was of it drifting up toward him.

With the patience of his people he lay motionless on the exposed slope, hidden only by the scrub, letting time go by. He ignored the penetrating cold, confident that the clothes he wore wouldn't let him freeze, ignoring the fact that they couldn't keep him comfortably warm.

Slowly the caribou moved up the slope. Then for a while they moved down and farther to his right. For a time, maybe an hour, half of them stayed out of sight.

Then, after two hours, maybe even three, they began moving up again, parallel to and much closer to the draw by which he had made his approach. If they stayed on this course, they would pass a mere hundred yards in front of him.

Another half hour, maybe an hour, slipped by.

Then the wait ended. Led by a big bull, the band began to string out, traveling quickly, heading across below him.

Dave passed the lead bull, shooting the next in line, through the ribs just back of the shoulder, where the meat lies thin. The animal ran thirty yards then dropped, motionless.

The band burst. Two animals came toward him in panic. He dropped them both with rapid shots.

The caribou fled everywhere now across the slope. Dave scrambled up, stiffly, to try again. A bewildered yearling had hesitated a little longer than the rest. Dave's carbine fired once more. The yearling crumpled.

Filled with relief at being able to move again and with the satisfaction that followed the kill, he scrambled back to his dogs and brought them out of the draw and down to his new supply of meat. He spilled the cavity of each carcass in turn, then gathered all four together. Then he loaded the two of medium size, leaving the largest bull and the yearling for the second trip. At that he had a good load, for these were the mountain caribou, half as large again, if you picked the best, as the barren ground caribou further north.

He stopped to consider the meat he was leaving and to glance away to camp, perhaps three miles distant, the way he'd come. He'd make good time going down, poor time coming back. The sun, lightly obscured behind a thin overcast which had persisted since the storm that broke the cold snap, rolled close to the horizon and soon would sink beneath it in the long angle of its winter path. There would be no time to come back for the remaining meat.

To the north the sky was clear. And the wind was still, perhaps just beginning to drift out of the north. Dave wet a finger which chilled on the north side when he held it up. Yes, the drift was out of the north.

It would be colder again tonight, perhaps forty degrees below. Sometimes the cold air settled back in quietly as the westerly air ran out of push, without the preliminary north wind blow. It could be sixty below again after three or four days of a mere four-mile-an-hour drift out of the Arctic.

Dave cut enough of the scrub to cover the remaining carcasses. Then he turned his dogs the hundred yards into the draw, then down the long trail they'd made coming up. On the downhill pull, Dave had to ride the brake—the iron hook behind the toboggan which a man drove with his foot to varying depths into the snow and ice to hold a runaway team, or one going downhill.

Darkness closed in during the next few minutes and in the course of that time Dave pulled into camp.

Harrison hadn't returned. Although Dave had thought he would have been back and had worried about the two whitemen being alone, his concern grew greater now. Harrison had become reasonably useful but he was still hardly fit to be out after dark, and Dave felt certain he knew it. Something had to be wrong.

He unloaded the meat and fed his dogs in their harness. He boiled some tea and ate quickly from the pot of food he'd left on the stove for Bill to keep warm, then put extra socks inside his moccasins.

As he gathered a couple of blankets from his bedroll and all the spare socks he could find in Harrison's dunnage, he instructed Bill: "You stay up and keep fire till I come back. No matter how late. You got wood to last all night."

Then he gathered a few more essentials, the little bits of this and that to save a life perhaps somewhere on a frozen slope in the night: a piece of canvas, a little grub, a tea billy, enough dry wood to make a small, thrifty fire for a few precious hours.

He turned his dogs out of camp, onto Harrison's tracks. Refreshed with food, they ran out swiftly. Dave's worry now was to keep to Harrison's tracks and to sort between yesterday's and today's, a fairly easy matter unless his dogs made the mistake for him and he wasn't quick enough to realize it in the dark.

For the first three miles, Harrison had walked the same track both days. Then, near the south side of the valley where a steep side draw brought in a large creek, the trails forked. The fresher tracks went up the draw to the south.

Dave put the dogs on this and they slowly ascended in the middle of the draw, a draw alternately wide then narrow, steep then flat. All the way he was able to travel beside the creek instead of on its ice, but always at greater difficulty.

The creek, unlike the larger river, was subject to overflow, when water, choked by the penetration of frost into the stream bed, was forced up by its own pressure to spill over the surface of the ice.

It had been against this danger that Dave had warned Harrison, and he suspected now what might have happened. Harrison, impatient to make good time, would have avoided the easy walking on the ice only at first. Then, when the harder travel along the banks had frustrated him thoroughly, he would have taken to the ice.

And here there was no firewood. In this long stretch of the valley where the timber stood sparse and scattered, a man could be an hour, perhaps two, away from firewood.

Dave avoided the ice, keeping his dogs scrambling in the rougher going. At that it was faster than Harrison could walk and they were bound to catch up with him soon, either overtaking or meeting him. Twice, Dave saw the telltale shade of newly soaked snow on the ice to his right.

He saw also that more frequently, Harrison had gone onto the ice to avoid difficult stretches of walking along the side. In the scrub, the snow lay not quite deep enough to cover the hummocks of the tundralike creek bottom and to afford good snowshoeing; yet it lay too deep for easy going in moccasins alone.

It was when his dogs climbed a short steep rise that gave way to a basinlike stretch of valley leading away to a saddle in the high ridge to the south that Dave saw the snowshoes, upright, planted in the snow, next to a clump of scrub.

He pulled up the dogs and walked ahead. The tracks told the story clearly. Harrison had for some time been walking on the ice and here, tiring of carrying the snowshoes and convinced he

193

could get by without them, he had walked off the ice to stand the shoes where he would see them on the way back. His tracks led away again up the creek.

Walking back to the rear of his toboggan, Dave discovered something else he'd failed to notice all the while he'd been traveling southward, his back to the brilliant northern sky and the fiery sweep of the northern lights. The temperature had dropped faster than he'd guessed it would, and the north wind drift had become a light breeze. He estimated forty-five degrees below. While he traveled with his back to it, Harrison had to face it.

In another two miles he found Harrison, though he nearly went on by. Only the hesitation of the lead dog made him pull up, to search about in the moonlight for what the tracks might tell. The dogs had just cut Harrison's fresh trail, leading directly away from the creek. Following the new tracks, within a hundred yards they came on him.

He sat on the makeshift pack, his arms around his knees, his head down, moaning softly.

Before his feet lay the ruins of an attempt to make a fire: the ashes of the twigs Dave had put in his pack, the charred bits of scrub which had refused to burn, the last spent matches where numb fingers had let them drop.

Dave touched the moccasins. They were frozen solid.

"Harrison. It's Dave. You hear me?"

Harrison stirred, raised his head, and, glassy-eyed, let it drop.

There wasn't time to take him to camp. Dave fetched his wood and lit a fire at Harrison's feet. Then he brought the blankets, folding one into a pad which, by shifting Harrison about, he put beneath him. The other, he threw about his shoulders and back.

And as he worked to save the life, he came as close to cursing as his nature ever let him, for even after the moccasins had been drenched in the overflow, disaster needn't have followed.

Harrison wore good woolen underwear beneath a woolen shirt and a stout mackinaw. Since the traveling would keep him warm, he could spare the woolen undershirt to tear into two foot wrappings. Then the canvas of his makeshift rucksack, lashed on with thongs quickly made from the moccasins, would make an outer

194

wrap sturdy enough to let him go on, slowly, but onward all the same.

But knowing how is as vital as knowing what, and Harrison had not known how.

Next Dave fetched the canvas and threw this over Harrison's back and shoulders. Then he cut two of the most substantial sticks he could find amongst the scrub, about four feet long, to make an A-frame with which he drew the canvas forward over Harrison's head.

He now had Harrison sheltered from the wind by an effective leanto, which served also to hold and gather around him the heat of the little fire.

The fire Dave kept small, adding one precious stick at a time, making no more heat than Harrison could use, ensuring he'd have enough heat for as long as possible.

Then Dave took the moccasins off, and the socks. He worked slowly, letting the fire soften the frozen socks, so as not to damage the skin.

The toes were solid and the frost had penetrated the forward part of the foot. The heels, too, were touched on the bottom, but the insteps remained pliable.

Dave unhitched the toboggan, laying it on edge alongside Harrison, extending past his feet and the fire to further gather in the heat and keep the wind from eddying around the exposed skin.

When he'd done all he could with fire and shelter, he heated food and water. Harrison would be in terrible pain when he began to revive, and he was anxious to get hot tea and food in him quickly.

But Harrison was tough physically, just as he was stubborn in his heart, and as the heat of the fire and the makeshift shelter reversed the loss of heat from his body, he grew aware of his surroundings again, and the presence of Dave.

Seeing this, Dave urged tea on him, holding the cup to his mouth, begging him to drink. Once the pain began, nothing could be done until it was over.

Harrison started on the tea. At first it was too hot to bear and

Dave cooled it with snow. The next cup was easier and Dave followed it up with the hot food.

Harrison became fully conscious, moving his arms freely, shifting his weight a little. Then the pain began and Dave removed the tea and grub.

There are few agonies worse than thawing flesh, and few sounds worse than the cries of a man in the night on a windswept northern slope beseeching relief in vain.

Twice he begged Dave to take away the fire, and twice Dave shouted at him through his cries to hang on, his life depended on it.

Long past the middle of the night, when the carefully rationed firewood was almost gone, the pain subsided and the exhausted Harrison spoke again in his own voice: "I'm all right now."

Dave dared not put on the socks he'd brought, for the feet were bound to swell and blister. He therefore righted the toboggan and hitched the dogs. Then, setting the toboggan beside Harrison, he laid one blanket on the floor of the toboggan and moved Harrison onto it, flat on his back.

The other blanket he wrapped about the man's feet, and the canvas he threw over him, tucking it down securely at the sides.

Then, stowing the tea billy and other bits of gear, he set the dogs back the way they'd come, to follow their own trail into camp.

It was almost daybreak when they pulled up before the tent.

Chapter 35

They couldn't think of traveling for many days. Harrison's feet were a blistered mess, keeping him awake at night and Dave as well, for the fire wanted stoking so that in the warmth Harrison would have no need of the covers he couldn't bear upon the skin of his damaged toes and heels.

Dave fetched the rest of the caribou meat at once, for staying ahead of hunger by a long margin had grown more essential now than ever. Now they couldn't make a forced trek to Little Salmon if the food ran low. He held the dogs to a close ration, wasting nothing from the blood-stained snow on the hillside.

He kept ahead on wood, too. Each day, going farther from the tent, he felled some of the dry wood that had caused him to choose this place. Then he took more than as much green aspen from a stand down the river on the north side, perhaps a mile away. This burned well once the dry wood had the fire going, and he brought it in with the dogs.

Bill volunteered to spend his days cutting wood, seeing how little Dave slept at night. But Dave declined the offer. If Bill cut himself with the axe, there would be two invalids to one healthy man, and survival for all three would be increasingly difficult.

Now, at least, Dave could go out of the camp and leave the two alone. Bill had learned to do a few chores in the cold, so he was fit to stay out for a while each day, and Harrison couldn't get up on his feet. He had to move on his hands and knees and Dave built a latrine for his use close by the rear of the tent.

Dave scanned the open slopes in hope of more caribou, at the same time setting out snares for rabbits in the patch of timber around the campsite.

He mixed their own diet from beans, caribou and rabbit, with only occasional bannock, for the flour was almost gone.

The dogs he fed mainly on caribou meat and rabbits. The fresh fish had been used up, and what dry fish was left he planned to keep for the journey home.

Harrison's feet did not infect, nor turn gangrenous, and Dave regarded this with a primitive awe. As the feet improved, he gave up a half-formed idea that before something worse happened he ought to load Harrison in the toboggan and in long, forced days return quickly to Little Salmon where the responsibility for both the whitemen, of which he was utterly weary, might be handed over to Simpson at the post.

Instead, he decided not to travel until Harrison could walk again, even if not well—but enough that he wouldn't have to ride the footboards for most of the trip.

The weather was settled. The brilliant nights, fired by the northern lights, fell to a brittle sixty degrees or more below. The days, dazzling in sunshine, moderated to fifty, as close as Dave could reckon.

In the long nights, as in the days, little moved in the land as it lay in the grip of the arctic air. The long reach of the river valley in the moonlight, the snow-covered mountains rising away to the north and south: to the eye these harbored little more than the tent, half-obscured in a stand of frozen spruce, its faithfully tended fire sending a column of smoke skyward; there was little to be heard other than the howl of the wolves in their endless hunger and the whimpers of the dogs in camp.

When Harrison at last became able to tend his own fire, Dave took to sleeping through the nights so as to have energy in the daytime. Then Bill could tend the fire while Harrison slept and Dave kept his persistent vigil for the longed-for bit of movement on the slopes.

One morning a single caribou passed within a mile of camp, traveling westward, seeking to rejoin the band that had doubtless scattered after an attack by wolves, perhaps last night, perhaps yesterday.

And the caribou that escaped the wolves did not escape Dave,

198

who devoted half a day to a deadly cautious stalk, planned from his first step out of camp to the dropping of the hammer on the firing pin to permit of no error.

But ten dogs can eat one small caribou in one day, and finally Dave had to choose between breaking camp in cold weather with Harrison's feet still not ready for walking or making a greater effort to kill meat.

He chose the latter. After cutting several days' wood supply one day he left with his dogs and a light outfit early the next.

By early afternoon he was through a narrow pass and into the next valley to the north. There he intercepted more than a hundred caribou, killing six of the largest as he fired rapidly into the disbanding herd.

He spent the next two days bringing in the meat and the whole camp ate heartily, dogs and men alike, for the following week. Dave intended to break out at the end of that week, regardless of weather.

He had been assuming, he realized now that his own decision was formed, that Harrison was ready to go back, whether his purpose in coming here had been realized or not—and it was pretty clear it had not.

So on the evening of the day that Harrison first wore socks and moccasins again to take a short walk around the camp, Dave made his intention clear.

They were in the tent with supper over and the ration of candlelight for the evening was almost done, when Dave spoke up. "You feet okay to travel soon. Three, four days, we start back to Little Salmon."

Harrison faced him solidly, the old powerful will returning as surely as the strength to his feet. "I've come a long way, just to go back."

"We low on grub."

"You can get more. I told you at the start, we were going to be out maybe most of the winter."

That was true, and if all three of them had been capable, each one taking on any variety of necessary work, particularly in maintaining the food supply, it would be easy to abide by. But with one man fending for three, it couldn't be done. But how could he get it across?

"We out of dry wood here soon. We have to go back four, five mile anyway."

That was exploratory and defensive. Harrison treated it as such.

"Or go on to the next good campground."

Dave tried another approach. "You sure you in the place you lookin' for?" Harrison hadn't had the map out since he'd frozen his feet, and Dave wondered if he'd lost it.

Dave had found ground now with more meaning to Harrison. After a long silence the other replied: "The job that son-of-a-bitch did on this map, I'll never be sure."

Dave levered his advantage, now he saw he had one. "There's hell of a bunch them kind maps around. Some bad men, he make him up just to sell him for few dollars."

The silence dragged this time, long and smoldering as Harrison brooded over his defeat. Dave feared that in his stubbornness Harrison would suddenly explode, demanding that they stay; for complying with others, or with circumstance, seemed hateful to him.

So very gently Dave spoke once more, the last time that evening. "We go to bed now." And he blew out the candle.

Nor did he raise the subject further. He merely went on in obvious preparation for leaving, and when the morning came, he made the simple announcement and rolled his bedding. The others did the same.

The trip to Little Salmon went rapidly and without event. They traveled long days, making the briefest of camps. Dave pushed them hard, all of them, the dogs, Bill, the still-injured Harrison and himself. Both Bill and Harrison had to ride the toboggan frequently to keep up, but Dave never rode, not more than one foot on the footboard and the other foot pushing.

When they reached the settlement they were completely exhausted, dogs and men alike.

Chapter 36

Dave took the whitemen to the trader's, then tethered the dogs. He took a meal with his people, then shortly after dark went to seek a settlement of this unhappy business, so that he might go again about his own life.

He joined the three men at a table in a room to the rear of the post.

"You had quite a trip," Simpson observed, offering him coffee.

Dave nodded his acknowledgment, accepting the coffee.

Harrison, rested by the meal and a return to surroundings more usual to him, had recovered the thrust to his jaw and the belligerence with which his eyes sought out others.

Dave wished there were no business to do, but there was business and it had to be done. Still, he waited for others to start it.

Simpson did so. "What you fellows plan to do now?" It was enough of a start. It triggered Harrison.

"How the hell do I know what I'm going to do now? I spent half the winter going where I wanted to go and coming back without a chance to locate what I went for. And you ask me what I'm going to do now. Maybe, I'll hire an Indian with guts to stay out there and go back again!"

"All right, Mr. Harrison! All right! Just hold on. First of all, you hired the best man you could have found. Secondly, I don't know what you're looking for, but if you're prospecting, it's your own damn fault if you insist on trying to locate something in the middle of winter."

Harrison had a fight on, and he rose to it gladly. "Look, man, I've got a perfectly good map! All I needed was time and some men to help me. And what have I got? That useless bastard there

201

and an Indian who can't think about anything but running home to his . . . his family."

Simpson was his match. Calmly, he put the next obvious question: "Couldn't Dave figure out from your map where to take you?"

A silence followed. Dave used it to sip his coffee. It wasn't his question to answer.

"Well, couldn't he? Couldn't you, Dave?"

Dave let it pass. Finally Harrison said: "I didn't show him the map."

"You didn't show him the map?" Simpson's incredulity dripped from his words.

"Why should I, for God's sake? I paid good money for this map and the information that went with it. I'm not letting every Siwash . . ."

"Shut up, Harrison! Get hold of yourself. From what you've said, Dave saved your life. The least you can do is treat him with respect." Then quietly: "Look, Harrison. The country is full of maps to prospects of every kind. Not a summer goes by that one, or two, or half a dozen fellows go through here clutching a piece of paper they bought from some old timer who's too old to go back but swears he was just on the verge of a find the last time he left some far valley or creek.

"Sometimes they're plain frauds, but most of the time they were passed on in good faith that there was something there—though usually there isn't. You have to realize the way men think in the Yukon. It's only a short time since everything happened over on the Klondike, you know."

Harrison jumped up and grabbed his dunnage, spilling it out. He located his map, then threw it on the table.

"All right! What do you make of that? But remember, it's mine."

Simpson hardly glanced at it. He laid it out carefully in front of Dave. "Let's see what *Dave* makes of it. He knows the country."

Now that the elusive piece of paper lay in front of him, Dave found it a disappointment. He'd come to expect something exceptional and it was anything but.

202

It showed the main stream of the Yukon quite clearly, and the general shape of the Little Salmon and Big Salmon rivers, including the confluence with the North Big Salmon.

Then up the Big Salmon, on one of only three side streams shown to the south, to the left of the stream and an undefined distance away was a mark and some writing.

He shoved the map to Simpson. "What that say?"

Simpson looked at it. " 'Silver-lead outcrops along strike to . . .' I don't know what the last words are."

" 'Top of ridge,' " Harrison put in.

Dave studied the map again, seeking an answer to the critical question, how far up the Big Salmon. He traced the curves on the map with his finger, and the river itself in his mind.

"Silver-lead, is he same thing you call galena?"

"Well, pretty much the same thing. That right, Harrison?"

Harrison shrugged. "He said silver-lead on the map and that's all he talked about. I'm no prospector."

"Somebody say two, three places south side Big Salmon you find galena. He lies right on top the ground. Lots prospector go all around over there but can't find how he goes. Can't figure out how he could make mine."

Harrison came to life. He grabbed the map. "You mean this country here is common knowledge?" He emphasized his words with a thrust of his finger on the map, defiantly.

"I not sure what you mean. But I know lots prospector been all over up there."

"Why the hell didn't you say so?"

Simpson jumped in again. "You didn't really give him a chance, Harrison. You were so damn anxious to keep him in the dark, it's a wonder he got you as far as he did. You can't blame him if you wouldn't trust him to start with."

Harrison threw the map on the table and stood up. "You can have the damn thing. I'm pulling out and I won't be back. Dave, you can take me over to Yukon Crossing tomorrow and you can keep the dogs and sleigh I bought."

Dave wondered what he could do with the extra dogs and the

toboggan, but he knew what he could do with the money that was due to him.

"We leave in the morning, Mr. Harrison, so we have to settle up now. You can just make my pay to Mr. Simpson here 'cause I owe the store and I got to go trapping."

"Pay you! What the hell for? What did I get out of all this but frozen feet? If you'd . . ."

But Simpson was in at once, quietly again, the way he did when he meant business in the most serious way. "Harrison, you owe Dave for two months at a hundred dollars a month, and you don't leave till you pay it. And you're getting by cheap. It isn't half the going rate."

Harrison fetched his wallet and gave Simpson the money.

At the sight of the money, Bill made the first positive statement Dave had yet heard from him.

"That's my money, Ted. You better give it back to me now we're not partners any more."

Harrison spun on him. "You shut up!"

Simpson looked from one to the other and the plaintiveness in Bill's face must have made him suspicious.

"Bill," he said, "you better tell me about that money."

Harrison started but Simpson silenced him: "Harrison, I don't know who you are or where you came from, but if Bill here wants to tell us something about that money, he's going to tell us. If you don't let him, then *you'll* be telling it—to the police in White-horse."

Bill spilled the words out, eagerly. "It's my money. He said we'd get rich on this silver in the Yukon. He had a map from a prospector he'd met, and he knew where it was. But he said he needed a partner."

"To buy the tickets to the Yukon and buy the outfit, the grub, the toboggan, the dogs," Simpson finished it for him.

"Yes. That's right. Just like that. How'd you know?"

"Oh, I just guessed." But, of course, such partnerships had been a big part of the traffic on the river for some years, and Simpson had seen dozens of them. He'd very nearly been talked into one or two himself. "Well, Harrison, the partnership's over I guess. Bill, when are you going back out?"

"I'll wait till spring if I can, Mr. Simpson. If you'll let me stay, that is." The childlike eagerness entreated Simpson. Dave wondered if he should leave. This part really wasn't his business. But he didn't find an opening to get up.

"You can stay. The money now, Mr. Harrison."

Harrison threw the wallet on the table, much as he had the map. Simpson handed it to Bill, who turned it out on the table. There was about three hundred dollars, in worn American currency.

"I guess you own some dogs and a toboggan, Bill, as well as anything else your money paid for. Don't you agree, Harrison?"

"What the hell am I supposed to do? Walk out of the Territory?"

Bill's face registered that he had not thought of this. He split the money in even piles. "Here. You can have half of it. That's fair, because we were in our trouble together."

The ways of whitemen were too much for Dave. He told Harrison they'd leave in the morning, and he went back to be with his people for the night.

The next day he set out with his own team, a light outfit, and Harrison in the toboggan. He made Yukon Crossing in a day and a half, delivering to the lodge keeper there an envelope he'd been handed by Simpson.

On reading the letter he said to Dave: "You're to take back the stuff these men left in my cache when you went out of here." Then to Harrison: "You're heading for Whitehorse? The stage just left, it shouldn't even be out of sight. Dave, run your dogs out and catch up to those horses. Otherwise, Harrison will have to wait here several days."

"Listen. I've got some of my own stuff in that cache. I got to get that."

"Okay, Dave, you tip that toboggan of everything, then go to beat hell. Tell the driver I said to come back. Hurry now!"

Dave tipped the toboggan to empty it on the snow, then righted it and sped his dogs across the river. The stage was gone from sight, but from what had been said he knew he could catch it in minutes.

But he doubted the point of it. The stages carried mail and they wouldn't delay for a passenger. How he happened to know, he'd been at Upper Laberge the previous winter when a woman had taken sick in the village there. He'd gone out across the ice when the stage sleigh came into sight to ask the driver to hold up for a few minutes. He had explained that the people were making the woman ready for the trip to Whitehorse, and that they'd have her across in a toboggan right away.

But the driver had hied his horses and gone on. "Can't wait," he'd said. "Got mail on board. Tain't that far to Whitehorse. Take her in with y' dogs. Mail's got to go on time."

If the drivers couldn't wait ten minutes, it was a sure thing they couldn't turn their horses on the trail and go back on their tracks.

But he sped on to take the message, catching the stage within a mile and a half of the river.

"What's up, fella?" the driver demanded as he reined in the horses, stopping the sleigh.

"Man just come into Crossing. Wants to catch the stage to Whitehorse."

"Well, godamnit, he's too late. I can't turn back to pick him up."

Dave had expected as much. Then in explanation of himself: "I just bring you message. Mr. Ward, he say to tell you."

The driver hesitated and his expression changed. "Mr. Ward said for me to come back for this passenger? This fella, he's a whiteman?"

Dave nodded.

The driver swung the horses out in the unbroken snow, turning the sleigh back the way it had come. Dave fell in behind, letting his dogs set their own pace.

Back at the roadhouse, Harrison waited ready with a small dunnage and a bedroll. Mindful of Simpson's warning to leave everything else for his hapless partner, he had only his most essential belongings.

He boarded the sleigh without a backward glance.

And, resting his dogs as he watched the sleigh go out of sight, Dave felt more strongly than ever the implied inferiority of the Indian. A whiteman could come as a cheechako to the Territory, be a fool in it for most of two months, and yet still, by being a whiteman, turn a stage back.

It was not something a man could understand or even think about in the attempt to understand.

He could only feel it, deep inside.

Chapter 37

Once again, beyond all my expectations, I had been taken into the river valleys of the past, on a long journey into the yesterdays of Dave's life.

A silence followed the last reflective words on the puzzling contradictions of life. In that silence I slowly gathered myself once more into the present. The swish of the river current beyond the fringe of alder on the bank, the bit of light escaping from the stove draught to play in flickering leaps upon the canvas of the teepee, the fragrance of the spruce brush: these surrounded me again while I looked back on where we'd been.

"What about the fellow Bill? Did he go out in the spring?"

"He don't go out. I guess his money not enough by spring to buy him ticket. So he stays for long time, till he gets old. He has hard time to live, he hardly can use axe or shoot moose, but he makes out. Indian help him lots, shoot him moose, let him trap little bit for cash."

"Where'd he live? At the village?"

"For little while. Then he lives back in bush. You 'member that cabin we look at one day when we at Little Salmon?"

"Yes. And you said the guy went crazy, the police had to take him out."

"Well, that's him. Some boys help him make that little cabin, and that's where he live for long time till he can't take it no more."

So there was the end of it, and we took to our sleeping bags, defying the passing river to call on us again till we were ready. We slept so late that we hadn't enough day left to set off. So we gathered wood and feasted well then slept again through a whole night and into another morning, rising with the dawn, chiding our-selves that we had lost the discipline of the traveler.

"We keep this up, the ice'll be running before we make the mouth of the Stewart."

Dave, still in his undershirt and with his hair rumpled from sleep, savored his mug of tea.

"This way, we savin' on candle."

We made a late start out of there then, threading our way through the multitude of islands that lie between Yukon Crossing and Minto Landing, another settlement of the old steamboat days, oc-cupied now by a handful of Indian trappers in winter, a few more families in summer at fish-drying time.

We might have made Fort Selkirk within the day but for the late start. As it was, we camped below Minto Landing, then drifted into Fort Selkirk the next day. Time had become expend-able: we paid it out in careless quantities, buying cheap at the price the lazy enchantment of the river and its passing banks.

Fort Selkirk lies deserted but for the smoke of one cabin, that of Danny Roberts, his wife and daughter; Danny is a Selkirk In-dian trapper, who stays on here in this all-but-forgotten place, surrounded by yesterdays, shorn of tomorrows.

The remains of the settlement lie strung along the bank, a high bank well above river level, overlooking the wide bar-strewn stretch of the Yukon across from the confluence with the Pelly.

Now there is only the remnants of a barracks block, a motley lot of cabins and caches, an old schoolhouse still sheltering the wooden benches of a last century classroom, and a striking Angli-can church of native timbers: these are Fort Selkirk today. Here in the days of the river many lives were lived, much laughter and sor-row, much love and fear felt, all by people who finally, with the passing of the river boats, abandoned this place of their living.

Robert Campbell was the first whiteman to come here. An ad-venturing Scotsman, of the breed who gave their best years to the Hudson's Bay Company for little reward and no gratitude, he came with a small party by foot and canoe into the Pelly drain-age over the divide from the Mackenzie, by Frances Lake, in the first years after 1840.

He established the posts of Frances Lake and Pelly Banks, but they did not satisfy him. They did not reach far enough into the trading territory of the warlike Tlingit, and thus, within forbidden ground, he put up Fort Selkirk, a modest outpost, bare of comforts, since every effort to supply it was given over to trade goods. No stockade this; rather a building or two, dwelling quarters and storage cache, no stove but a fireplace, fashioned of stone and clay.

I had heard the story of Fort Selkirk in several versions in the Indian tradition. What little comes from Campbell's meager journals supported most of the story passed down over a hundred years in Indian fashion. So does the record of the common practices of the Hudson's Bay Company.

We made a tea-break stop on an island in the Pelly mouth, and lounging beside our fire, I nudged Dave's version out of him.

"Tell me about Fort Selkirk the first time, Dave," I said. "When the Hudson's Bay came down the Pelly." You are my storyteller now, I thought, just as your maternal uncle was perhaps your storyteller, and you cannot fail to tell me, nor I to listen. And I will listen on your every word, difficult though it is for you to pick your way about in this foreign tongue, for when you are my storyteller, you have accepted me, for a while at least.

"It is long time when he first comes, that Hudson Bay. Call him Campbell, that Hudson Bay man.

"Before he comes, coast people bring stuff they get from whiteman, they trade him on Pelly Indian 'n they trade him up Carmacks way.

"Coast Indian is hard to trade, is hard on stick Indian. He wants all kinds fur, mostly he wants marten 'n he give little stuff, maybe little axe and knife 'n stuff like that, but he don't give gun, not much he don't give gun. Mostly, he keeps gun for himself 'n he boss stick Indian around pretty bad." Stick Indian. Odd, that phrase, so often applied by the people themselves to the Athabascans.

Dave went on: "This is place near here, where coast Indian come to trade, before Fort Selkirk. It is trade place for coast Indian to get fur from stick Indian.

"Coast Indian, Tlingit Indian, he boss him around pretty bad, 'n one big chief he don't stand it no more 'n one time they kill maybe five, six them Tlingit Indian.

"He kill him 'n they have one hell of a time 'cause they won't pay for kill them Tlingit, 'n maybe them Tlingit goin' kill lots them stick Indian, so them stick Indian hide."

Dave paused to think some more about his story and how to tell it, so I threw some wood on the fire to make sure he knew we were going to stay as long as he needed.

Then he continued: "Maybe four, five years them Tlingit come back that same place for trade. But first he goin' make them Indians pay for kill them Tlingit. Maybe goin' make him pay lots fur.

"So them Indians knows them Tlingit goin' make him pay, 'n he stays in bush. He sees them Tlingit, but he don't come out. 'N them Tlingit, he knows them Indian there but he can't see 'em.

"Well, long time those Tlingit want that fur pretty bad, so he say he goin' forget about make him pay for kill them boys, 'n when he say that, that big chief of stick Indian, he come out 'n he make deal with them Tlingits, they goin' trade again.

" 'N he makes pretty good deal. He's big chief that one, even he got no gun 'n them Tlingit got gun, muzzle-loader gun them days, he makes good deal for them stick Indian. That Tlingit, he wants that fur pretty bad.

"Well, after while that Hudson's Bay come, that one Campbell. He's comin' down Pelly 'n he meet them Indian 'n he make big friends with that chief, that one makes deal with Tlingit.

"Then he makes Fort Selkirk. I don't know when he makes Fort Selkirk, but it's long time now. Maybe my daddy he's little boy when is Fort Selkirk that first time.

"So that chief, he tell 'em, you trade now with Hudson's Bay, 'n Campbell he got all the stuff 'n them Indians they trade there.

"He trades them gun 'n powder 'n they sure glad to get gun 'n powder. Only he cheats them little bit on that gun 'cause you got to pile fur till he's high as gun, 'n that gun he's maybe foot longer just so he makes big pile of fur to trade."

The trade-gun story is legend across the North. The guns, deliberately long in the barrel, cost the Bay perhaps two dollars a piece to have made: the furs piled high enough to match that

211

length brought thousands of dollars on the London market. But it is an old story, reflective of much that made up the relationship of trader to Indian in the North. In fairness to the Bay, it must be said that the cost of transporting those guns across a continent and over a vast divide and taking the fur back the same way was no mean sum either.

"But he pretty good man just the same, 'n them Indians they gettin' along fine, they tradin' with Campbell.

"But them Tlingit, he still comin' with stuff to trade for fur, but he don't get much fur for his stuff any more because Campbell he got all that stuff too 'n them Indians, they tradin' with Campbell.

"So that Tlingit, he come one time, maybe 'bout three four years, 'n he scare him all away 'n he burn that Fort Selkirk. Them Indians 'n Campbell, they seen they can't stop him 'n they run away 'n them Tlingits, they burn all that stuff 'n they burn store 'n everything."

There was a pause, then: "Maybe, they take some of that stuff. Anyway, Campbell, he come back 'n he see what they done 'n he's goin' to follow 'em up, maybe fight with 'em. But that old chief he stop him, he says no use, only goin' make more trouble.

"So Campbell says, okay, only he got no grub or outfit left 'n that chief he gives him some grub 'n he help him get started back up Pelly. 'N Campbell, he leaves the country 'n he don't come back, but 'fore he goes he says to chief, you got no whiteman name so I give you my name 'n so he gives him his name, 'n that chief he's got that name Campbell 'n he can use it.

" 'N Campbell, he don't come back. That chief, after that, he's run kind of a store, he's get fur from Indian down Dawson way 'n up Pelly 'n he trades with them Tlingit."

Dave fell silent and I mulled over his story. He'd given me something I hadn't heard before, the relationship with the stick Indian chief. It is not hard to imagine the importance of that friendship in the attempts of a lone whiteman coming into the country by the back door and stealing the trade out from under the noses of the Tlingit.

212

We gathered the tea things then and put out in the canoe. It must have been with little more than tea things that Campbell had gone back up the river, only he had the current to pole and line and portage against, all the way to Pelly Banks and beyond.

He made his way back to Fort Simpson, and then, the winter on him, snowshoed to St. Paul—all the long miles to Minnesota—to reach a communication point from which to send out a message asking for permission to rebuild the fort.

But this was denied; and Fort Selkirk came to life again only on the eve of gold rush when the infiltration of prospectors and the hardiest of missionaries once more brought significance to this pleasant piece of benchland at the confluence of the upper Yukon's largest rivers.

With gold rush came the soldiers, the Yukon Field Force, by way of the Stikine and the height of land to Teslin Lake. Here at Fort Selkirk they quartered, to impress Canadian sovereignty on the wild American prospectors who made up better than half the stampede.

And then Fort Selkirk settled down to the life of a river settlement: police post, trade point, mission center, schoolhouse of sorts because it was larger than most, gathering place for Indians when they weren't out in the hills for fur or up and down the river drying fish.

As the gold fields waned and the very word Klondike lost its magic, so also did Fort Selkirk become gradually only an ordinary place in the minds of men.

The Bay came again, after gold rush, but stodgily. Now their store was just one more country store in a chain of stores that were the paunchy middle age of that company of adventurers granted their charter so long ago by the King of England.

No incredible Scot came this time, who'd once survived an earlier winter by chewing the rawhide lashings of his snowshoe harness. There were no hostile Indians, who'd never seen a whiteman to be won over, and no running of white water in Granite Canyon on the Pelly now in fragile skin canoes. This time the Bay came in the persons of manager and clerk, who would deal as readily in antidotes for stomach acidity as they would in fur.

Then the highway went in from Whitehorse north, crossing the Pelly some thirty-five miles upstream.

And this brought an end again to Fort Selkirk, a more mundane end this time, without half the excitement of a pillaging party of Tlingit warriors. The Selkirk Indians moved upstream to Pelly Crossing or Minto Landing on the Yukon, the police moved out to more active centers, the churches and school closed and the Bay packed up, leaving Fort Selkirk a second time.

How strange that quality in a deserted cabin, a vacant police post, or an empty church that will not fill again, which quickens in your mind how men once lived here, how they laughed and sang, feared and felt anger, worked and grieved, worshiped and sought comfort; and makes you forget all the smallness of men, seeing here only their courage and their faith with one another, in the harsh but wondrous North where brotherhood, between men whose origins were so vastly different as to be even in contradiction, flowered on the trail, along the banks of the rivers and in the lonely camps of a lonely land.

Chapter 38

The day we left Fort Selkirk, I suggested, over the noonday tea fire, that it was high time we did something about moose meat.

Dave agreed. "Now we in best moose country. All kinds slough and island. Any time, we find fat bull, maybe even dry cow."

Now I appreciated that dry cow bit. There's no denying it, a cow that had lost her calf in the spring, or hadn't successfully bred last fall and never had one, and therefore hadn't the burden of making milk all summer, made the very best meat eating in all these hills and valleys.

But the Territorial Game Administration had an ordinance prohibiting the shooting of cow moose, and a fine of up to five hundred dollars for being caught at it.

Hence my caution: "Now let's be careful about this cow moose stuff, Dave. I know she's pretty good eating, but she's also against the law."

Dave took a long drink of tea, then flicked the leaves in the bottom of the mug into the campfire. "But it's okay when she's dry." And he reached for the billy can to refill the mug.

I wondered what he meant: that he understood the law permitted the killing of *dry* cows, which it didn't, or that it made such good sense to kill dry cows that it was a matter of indifference that the law said you shouldn't—the law being a bit of a fool.

I recalled the words of the part-Indian woman who'd contributed no little to my raising back in the Cariboo country of British Columbia: "There's God's law and there's man's law. God's law says you shall not steal or rob and you got to obey that law. But it's only man's law that says you can't kill deer out of the season the government sets for it, so if you need some meat, you kill a deer."

Well, we needed meat regularly enough, and we sure did away with a heap of deer over the years. Still, there are many ways of looking at it, and I guess we can't all go around making our own laws.

The proper management of wildlife is built on a few principles that are not beyond the understanding of ordinary men. Game administrations do not always practice proper management, but where they do, the law stating what and when the man afoot in the hills may kill, grows out of these principles.

Since I was so frequently that man afoot in the hills, I'd been through the arguments often enough, and I ranged across them then in my mind.

To begin with, no species will survive without a big enough piece of the type of country suitable to its needs.

It may be tragic that buffalo hunters killed off the magnificent herds, which numbered in the millions, across the great plains of North America. But where would they live now, with the prairies fenced from end to end? Really, we don't have the buffalo any more simply because there is no place for them to live any more. Even had we effectively forbidden their slaughter, we would not have them—unless we had also let them keep the plains to live on.

The converse is that if you have enough suitable territory for a particular species, you'll have that species, and if the territory is good enough, you'll have an impossible job to get rid of the species: like the rabbit in Australia—the country suits him so well, you can't kill him off.

Further, there is a limit to the number of animals that any territory, however suitable, may support. Up to that limit, the reproductive power of the species will continually keep the population level up. Beyond it, natural limiting factors will drain off the surplus.

The natural limiting factor with the meat animals that men like Dave depend on—moose, caribou, deer—is the supply of food in the pinch of late winter. This is the lean time when there is the least food to go around. Too many animals sharing it means starva-

216

tion and death, helped on by the parasites, the ticks and the lung-worm and all the rest, that a healthy animal bears with equanimity, but a starving one cannot stand.

In this way, the processes of nature hold an animal population from exceeding that upper limit.

But nature is more remarkable than that. If a population of animals, the moose in central Yukon, for example, is forever bat-ting up against the limit of the territory's carrying capacity, it will, by over-using the willow shoots that are the winter staple, reduce the capacity of the land to produce food.

Enter the predator, in most cases the wolf. Enter the men who gather meat from the hills. If together they kill off for their use a sufficient number of animals, there will be room in the territory, food enough to go around, no late winter die-off and no undue pressure on the food sources.

Over in Alaska, the game administration made one of the classic mistakes of the century.

When the whitemen first came, prospectors and adventurers, their carelessness with fire caused vast acreages of white spruce tundra in southern Alaska to burn. This tundra is the territory of the barren ground caribou and what he seeks between the little spruce trees is the branching lichen. This is his food, and without it he cannot exist. As the fires burned out the lichen, which may not return for a hundred years, so it reduced the caribou herds, in very exact proportions.

Government, honorably fearful for the dwindling herds, for-bade all hunting except some stringently supervised hunting by natives. They also launched a campaign to wipe out the wolf, the life predator of the caribou, the wolf, who has lived in ecological partnership with the caribou since antiquity and beyond.

The caribou multiplied at first. Then, in their overwhelming numbers (in terms of what was left of the territory), they over-grazed the remaining lichen, reducing it even further. Then came die-offs, by thousands, and a sad round of more protection, more pressure on the lichen, and even more die-offs, as well-meaning administrators sought to head off the disaster their frantic reac-tions brought ever closer.

217

Fortunately, however, the biology behind the process began to be understood. After 1952, when a study disclosed the error of past programs, tolerance of the wolf and of hunting have helped to restore the balances. If these measures are taken far enough to take the pressure off the range, the lichen may return and one day great herds of caribou may again be seen in southern Alaska.

Well, what all this meant to Dave and me as we enjoyed the last of our campfire on a bar in the middle of the Yukon River somewhere below Fort Selkirk was that we knew jolly well a dry cow moose here or there wasn't going to do any harm to the moose herds of the Yukon River valley.

Dave knew it because his people had been using cows, bulls, calves, yearlings—anything they could get close enough to kill—for generations, and the moose were still there. I knew it because I understood enough biology to realize that no moose herd is ever seriously harvested on a "bulls only" law in country so sparsely populated by man as the Yukon Territory.

Of course, Dave had cause for a different attitude than mine to game regulations.

Like his fathers before him, he had been born into the hunting camps of his people, to live on the fish of the rivers and the animals of the forests and mountains, to take them whenever and however he could. Had it been made wrong in the old days of his people to kill this or that animal by some arbitrary law, it would have been wrong to survive, and that is preposterous.

Was it really different now?

The whiteman had not come as an invader or conquering enemy.

He had just moved in. As easy as that. He simply moved in.

Then before you knew it, he said it was his country.

Then he imposed on it his laws.

And he said, everybody is subject to these laws.

Indians, too.

The Indians found that he meant what he said, for a few saw the inside of the whiteman's jails and told others about it.

But the first whitemen were not surprised to find that the Indians lived by their fishing and their hunting. It seemed perfectly natural that fish, caught in the ingenious wheels in the river, should

218

dry by the thousands on racks in the sun along the banks of the Yukon, the Pelly, the Stewart, the Klondike and all the other rivers and streams of the western watershed, while the salmon runs were on.

It did not seem at all strange that these hunters, clad half in their own trappings and half in the trade clothing, should gather around the fires of their hunting camps in the fall and rejoice in the meat hanging from poles lashed from tree to tree, great stocks of meat against the long hunger of winter.

It was another generation of administrators in the whiteman's government, halfway through the twentieth century, who observed that there was nothing in the law about game animals that exempted Indians from its provisions, except for a fortuitous stipulation that Indians living north of the Arctic Circle may kill all the caribou they need, a necessity so obvious that a council of lawmakers could rejoice in their magnanimity and provide for it.

And ignorant whitemen in the towns raged about the wastefulness and depravity of the Indians: whitemen who had never struggled in a raw wilderness to survive, whitemen who had not been on the wrong end of a savagely destructive traffic in liquor.

But some kept their heads.

They spoke of aboriginal right, the compelling idea that a people whose continuity in a primitive survival stretched back into antiquity must have some right of use, exercised over thousands of years, not so easily done away with by the imposition of another's law. It was this idea—that a right could exist beyond the law and, therefore, be neither assailable nor supportable in the courts, but supportable in man's conscience—that could be applied on behalf of the Indians.

And conscientious game administrators, their hearts, more than most, committed to the Indian people, made rationalizations that simplified their task, and they did not seek to enforce laws inconsistent with the Indian way of life.

The Indian people, wisely, made no display, in all this debate, of what they knew was theirs. They only went quietly on, as best they could, pursuing the remains of a way of life, fragmented

219

though it might be after sixty years of unwitting destruction by the whiteman.

Even when one was warned by the Director of Game that he could trap here, look on the map, up this creek and to the summit here, but not on this other creek across the summit, definitely not there because that trapline belongs to such and such a whiteman, even then the Indian did not try to explain how his father and his grandfather and all his grandfathers as far as he knew had always hunted both sides of that mountain.

No, he just nodded agreeably and remembered to let a little time pass by and be more careful the next time. Besides, there was hardly a whiteman in the Territory he liked better than the Director of Game, always decent to an Indian, on his side somehow, in spite of this awkward nonsense he had just been explaining.

Now mind you, one thing did hurt. That was the time the government made a law, a sanctuary law they called it, and nobody, not even an Indian, could trap for fur or hunt for game in all the St. Elias Mountains southwest of the Alaska Highway, from the Haines Road to White River. People who'd trapped there all their lives, whose fathers and grandfathers had trapped there, were told one day they couldn't trap there any more at all.

That was hard to understand, even from the whiteman who had not come as a conquering enemy, but simply moved in.

But then one did not expect the things the whiteman did to be fair, necessarily, though most of what he did was more fair than that.

Our fire had gone out as we sat on the bar, longer than we had planned, each lost in his own thoughts.

"Dave," I said, "I am hungry for moose."

"Me, too," he replied, and we gathered the lunch things and went back to the canoe.

Chapter 39

The trouble with hunting as we were, drifting the river, was that really there were only two best times of the day: first thing in the morning and last thing at night.

At day's end you must worry about a campsite and enough daylight to settle into it, and this competes with hunting, especially since the very last light is the best of the last light.

Morning time, you're well off. You roll out early and cook by candlelight. You break camp to slip out on the water at first shooting light.

The wind is quiet and the air cold. A wisp of mist hangs over a sluggish slough or pond. Here and there you startle a duck as the current takes you, your paddle dipping only enough to keep you in the narrower, slower channels behind the islands.

For a long while the sun, as unhurried as you are, does not rise. Then the first cautious shafts of light spill over the eastern skyline, firing the yellow and orange of the frost-struck willow and aspen leaves.

If you have not seen a moose by now, the odds have swung a little against you. When old sun comes a little higher, finding his way through the tops of the mature spruce into the forest floor, the best is over.

But you are still in moose country, a fine stretch of river, all cluttered with islands and bars, back channels and quiet side streams. Must you drift through this in the lesser times of day? This is river for the magic hours.

Ashore with you then, on the main bank where the country looks likely and make camp again—never mind that you broke it out only three hours ago. For here you will laze about until late afternoon, and then begin scouting the bush behind the camp. As dusk approaches, you will grunt in low, infrequent deep sounds out of your belly somewhere, after your notion of what is most likely to bring a bull rampaging out of the willow swamps.

Or you will have a well-dried shoulder blade from an earlier kill, and you will bat this on the willow trunks.

And if no moose is charmed by all this rummaging about, nor found as you walk softly beneath the spruce canopy in a more mature piece of forest, why it's off to camp to stoke the fire and boil the tea. Then in the morning, up by candlelight and perhaps this morning will be it.

Now you aren't going far at this pace, but you're coming closer to a moose than you would by hurrying on. . . .

With all this more in mind now than anything else, I spoke to Dave over the rustling of the silt against the skin of the canoe: "We should camp early. We keep going, we'll run right out of moose country."

Dave had these matters in mind, too, only he'd already reached a decision, probably a couple of days back upriver. "We goin' camp on south side 'bout one mile."

It was a superb campsite. From it we scanned a thousand yards of an island across a quiet channel then, where the channel turned into the main river, the leading edges of a group of bars, all readily seen with binoculars.

Near the camp, a stream of clear water spilled out of the bank. Behind lay an immense flat land, estuary of the stream, and, I imagined, simply crawling with moose.

"Dave, you sure know your country."

"I been long time up and down river. I don't know where to camp now, I better quit lookin'."

With just time to boil the billy then go for an evening hunt, Dave took the upriver direction and I the down, assured by Dave I'd find a place to cross the stream, which, quite soon, I did.

The place was thick with sign. Tracks cut the moss wherever I walked, and the rich, fresh dung of the fat bulls, bulls ready to

222

quit eating and start breeding, their season being upon them, lay everywhere about.

I walked a long way, one cautious step at a time, two looks and a listen at every step. Then I grunted and beat a willow bush with a stick, following that with a silent wait of twenty minutes.

I made a long penetration back toward the hill, startling myself and a cow and calf when I least expected it, rounding a bend of the trail into a low-lying wet clearing where the water backed in from the river. The cow splashed out of sight, the calf at her flank.

Dusk was falling and my remaining sweep upriver then out to the bank below the creek raised nothing. With barely enough light left for it, I scanned the island, then the distant bars with my binoculars. Nothing.

I returned to the camp and there was Dave, pottering about at the fire.

"No luck?" I opened.

"Lots sign. No moose yet. But lots moose here. We goin' to kill moose now, sure." And he headed off to the creek for some clear, fresh water.

I set about fixing some grub. When Dave came back with the billy of water, I told him about the cow and the calf.

And so night found us, a long and pleasant night in which we rested in wait for the dawn.

Chapter 40

We broke that camp in the small hours. Dave wanted to drift the next stretch of river in the best of the morning then hold up at another useful ground.

Once more then, at first light, the canoe carried us in silence through the light mists that hung over the gentle streams behind and between the islands. The land stood still in the chill of the dawn, like the dew waiting with held breath for the sun to rise.

The bull and the cow were only a suspicious spot of black on the beach of a distant bar when first we saw them.

"Moose!" in hushed exclamation.

"Might, might not. You look with you binocular."

Dreading sound, I laid my paddle on the load then as cautiously drew the binoculars from beneath the canvas where they lay by the butt of my rifle.

Quickly focusing: "Moose. A cow and a bull, I think." Then in a moment: "Yes. A cow and a bull."

"We go down close. We go on bar. I hold canoe. You shoot."

I heard these hushed instructions, then fixed on the moments ahead.

The longest time of the hunt passes between the sight and the kill. Approach too quickly, you lose the quarry; too slowly, the quarry walks off in the willows never knowing the danger; approach not far enough, the shot is impossible; approach too close, it may never be made.

And all the while your heart pounds and your quickening breath, you imagine, can be heard for miles.

We drifted, paddling only enough to find the current that would set us ashore upstream of the moose.

The distance visibly closed as the animals became distinct, the rack on the bull towering over them both.

Seven hundred yards became six, then five.

Where along that bar lay fit shooting range?

At three hundred yards, the moose became aware of an object drifting with the current, but they were not alarmed.

At two hundred and fifty, as a man might reckon it with his senses fraying in anticipation, the first alarm showed. Heads thrown higher, the animals searched the wind.

Then the current set us toward the bar. Boldly paddling as we had to, we beached the canoe at perhaps a hundred and seventy, a hundred and eighty yards.

Dave stepped out, dropped on the sand beside the canoe, pulled her tight by the gunwale, and steadied her completely.

"Now shoot."

I moved from my seat only enough to put a knee in the bottom of the canoe and rest the rifle on the load. The recoil drove into my shoulder. The bull went down, perfectly struck high in the neck.

There was no calf with the cow and suddenly I was in a dilemma.

Dave wasn't. He waited for the explosion of the second cartridge.

In an anguish, I looked to see where his carbine lay. But of course, it was ahead of his place in the canoe. He'd left it there, knowing he wouldn't need it.

Could I pass him mine? Not a chance. The cow milled uncertainly about. She would go any second and in a second.

Oh, Dave, what a mess! I can't shoot that cow because the law forbids it, and you can't because you counted on me to do it and you haven't your carbine.

His bewildered face turned to me and for a moment I met his eyes.

The cow died as quickly as the bull, and right beside him.

Relief washed over me in floods. I stepped out of the canoe and together we pulled it firmly onto the sand.

"Sorry, I damn near messed that up, Dave."

His grin divided his face. "Oh, we kill him nice. Whiteman shoot bull and Indian shoot cow, and now we help each other skin him out." If I could have got it through my head how much went on in his, I'd have saved myself a hell of a pile of guesswork.

We dressed and skinned and quartered both animals, then loaded the quarters, laying sticks beneath and between the pieces to let air around the meat. We would camp again quickly, to hang my bull meat to cool, and bone out and strip Dave's cow for drying. Had the bar afforded a decent camp we might have stayed right there.

Well now, that freighter canoe began to sit in the water as though she was a freighter canoe. Not far off three quarters of a ton of meat in addition to that generous pile of outfit put her down where she was meant to go.

"Hey, Dave. Let's not shoot anything else before we camp. We'll sink!"

"That why we goin' dry that cow meat."

This next camp was as good as the last one; and to top it off, an old trail led back into the mountains to the south. Dave decided that since we needed some time to dry the cow meat, we might go for a short sheep hunt, just for a change of flavor.

We unloaded, going directly to work. We cut one very stout pole, spanning it between two trees, and from this we hung the quarters from the bull.

Then we made a drying rack, which took a couple of hours of cutting many thin poles plus several stout ones, along with posts and stakes until, what with available trees taken into use as well, we had enough horizontal poles seven feet off the ground to hold all the cow meat after it was cut into strips a few inches long and about as thick as a man's hand.

Then Dave made a light smoke fire under the rack to discourage any flies that might show up, although the weather had chilled off enough for flies to be an unlikely threat.

Then the camp was put together, the stove fire was lit, and a chunk of fat moose meat found its way into the pot. Unaged moose meat makes strong eating, but when you've lived much of your life killing the meat you eat you develop an appetite for strong flavors.

A long day had passed since we put out at first light, though by

226

the sun it was still afternoon. But it had been a busy day measured against the leisure of the journey before it. And so we savored this camp the more, resting weary muscles, watching the smoke drift up through the meat from the now-accomplished kill, and waiting in contentment for the meat in the pot to simmer well and tender.

Thus we passed a long evening. When the meat was cooked we ate it, sitting outside the teepee by the sputtering flames of the little smoke fire.

Idly, I thought ahead to tomorrow.

"We going to hunt sheep out of here?"

"Maybe tomorrow we take trail out of here. Trail goes into mountain from here."

Another thought formed in my mind, which was lazing around the same as the rest of me. "Maybe a bear gets into our meat while we're gone."

Dave thought about that, poking the fire with a stick from where he sat. "We take a chance. I think he's maybe full up on cranberry, and he leaves our camp alone so long we don't go away more'n one, maybe two days."

One or two days. Pretty short sheep hunt. "We get a sheep here one day out of camp?"

"Might. We see. Anyway, he's nice country back here. One place, you stand on top of whole world. I show you. We spike camp one night on mountain."

After that we found our way into our beds. I fell asleep with sheep in mountain valleys and bears in camp tromping around in the hidden byways of my mind, a dry cow moose browsing on the shoots of my conscience.

Chapter 41

We made up light packs for the journey: a little grub, a warm jacket, a piece of canvas each but not a sleeping bag—too heavy—some spare rope.

Everything else in camp we bundled into the remaining pieces of canvas, three bundles all told. Then we cut three long poles, tying a bundle to the end of each pole. With much heaving we raised the poles, tying each back to a tree with its butt against the tree butt, the pole leaning outward, suspending its load a good twenty feet off the ground.

"Pretty fair pole cache, huh, Dave?"

"He's okay. So long as bear don't want him too bad, he's all right."

Of course if a bear did come to maul the camp, it was our meat we'd lose. But that a man can replace: ripped sleeping bags and smashed gear would be a more serious loss with many miles of river yet ahead.

The trail led directly away from the river, along the bottomland of the stream that drained the valley up which it climbed. Long disused, it had overgrown and fallen in. We made slow passage for the first three hours.

Then abruptly the trail swung westward out of the bottomland, climbing the slope in a long easy rise, breaking out of the heavy growth into sparse mature spruce. Then in another half hour we came, as suddenly, into the alpine open on the sidehill of the valley, looking up into a magnificent basin, perhaps four miles across, that stretched away before us another five, perhaps six, miles to a high ridge that forked the basin into two tributary valleys.

We had climbed high in the steady gradient of the trail. We

228

were up in the wind, up in the mountains, up where the primeval sheep range. It was hard to imagine so much change from the river valley in so short a distance.

"From the river, you wouldn't realize this was so close." And the wind blew my words away, making them a whisper.

"He's big country."

Yes, he's big country. Another thousand feet above us, the western rim of the basin met the sky. Up there, when the time was right, the sheep could be found grazing high pastures among massive outcrops of rock.

We moved another forty yards to sit on a convenient shelf of rock while we searched the basin and the distant slopes for life, Dave with practiced eyes, I with my binoculars.

Nothing. Well, in all that expanse of range there must be something alive and moving, and indeed you know there is. But you don't necessarily see it.

Half an hour passed.

Then Dave spoke.

"We take this trail. He brings us out below big mountain in middle of valley." I could see where he meant. The high ridge that split the basin rose out of the basin at about our present altitude. While the trail would lead from our present position on the western slope to the basin floor at the foot of the ridge, it would lose no altitude in so doing.

"Then we go around, one each side, and we meet up top. You see where he's low behind big rock?"

The dividing ridge went away from us at first, then swung westward, hiding the valley beyond to the east. The low place Dave identified lay saddlelike behind a mile of rock and rubble and slopes fanning out from the outcrops.

"That's a long ways, Dave."

"Not so far as he looks. One side or other, we shoot sheep."

We struck off, now glancing down at the footing, now upward to the slopes around us. Soon a flock of ptarmigan, winter white yet still with the flecks of summer brown, rose up like a flurry of snow from the scrub. I had feasted, other years on other mountains, on these mountain fowl.

229

When we paused for breath, Dave read my thoughts. "Good thing we don't bring shotgun. You shoot ptarmigan, you scare away sheep."

"But if we don't shoot sheep, Dave, we'll wish we had the shotgun so we *could* shoot ptarmigan."

Dave never stopped watching the mountain slopes. "We shoot sheep all right."

Going so far, we'd better shoot sheep. The grub we'd brought had shrunk in proportion to a mere snack. I could have eaten the lot right then, and we hadn't stopped for lunch yet.

When would we stop for lunch? Old Dave kept going, and I began to believe he could walk on forever at that easy but persistent pace long after I would be a spot of grease on the trail where I'd expired. Almost twice my age, he seemed as ageless as his movements were effortless.

And thirsty. I could have drunk swamp water out of a moose track, but nowhere on this mountain slope was there a trickle. The snows of last winter had melted off, and even the moss was crunchy underfoot.

We came at last to water in the low ground where the stream came out of the western fork. I dropped prone, supporting my weight on my hands at the edge of the stream and drank up a quart of ice-cold crystal water.

Old Dave dropped his pack, filled the billy, then began scrounging around the low alder growth for enough dry bits to make a fire.

"You ever just drink plain water? You know, you get so damn thirsty you can't wait for tea?" I put the question while I helped gather fuel.

Dave crushed some twigs into a skillful bundle, then dropped to his knees with his back to the wind. "When you thirsty, tea so nice, he's better to wait. Indian likes tea. More he waits, better he likes him."

"Well, I sure like my tea, but I was so dry I wouldn't have kept out of that water if you'd had a mug full and waiting for me right beside that willow bush. I guess I'd make a pretty poor Indian."

Dave had the fire going on the first match and carefully added the larger sticks. I cut a green branch, leaving a piece of a fork attached for a hook, then picked up the billy with it, holding the billy in the flames.

Dave rested back on his heels. "Oh, you make good Indian, all right. You make better Indian than them young guys now."

I hadn't meant to touch on that, not seriously. We'd been talking lightly and I'd said that bit about making a poor Indian for a joke.

And I wanted to say something to make it light again, back into a joke, but I couldn't think what, so I said nothing; but in my mixed emotion I agonized for a man led to pass judgment on the deterioration of his people, feeling guilt in my own search for his acceptance.

I kept the billycan in the flames and hoped for the mood to pass, which of course it did; and then I wondered what it was I'd felt so strongly there, what notion of meaning had I imputed in a few casual words now gone, blown away in the wind across the mountain slopes.

Then tea was made and I drank my share, washing down the ration of moose meat.

It was afternoon by a fair bit when we reached the foot of the ridge and I secretly worried that we had too little daylight left to reach the saddle by dark.

But Dave had his plans made. "You walk around east side. He's longer, but he's better goin'. I go this way, but I take long time cause he's rough for walk. We come to top by dark. There's little water there and some brush in little draw."

"And what if one of us shoots a sheep?"

"Gut him out 'n keep on goin'. We both come back in morning 'n pack him out."

With that we parted.

I spent an hour picking a trail through the knee-high scrub, working around the toe of the slope, penetrating the valley; then another gaining depth along the valley floor, all the while watching the skyline to the right to identify the rendezvous and the slopes on every side for sheep.

It is a slow pace, this hunting pace. Each step deliberately taken, each foot placed where the glancing eye decides, the rougher clumps avoided, the pathlike way between the clumps is chosen well ahead.

A racing pulse destroys a standing shot; an hour of sweating brings on chill and depression when fatigue takes over.

The naked eye sweeps the landscape, then the binoculars come up to search a draw or the lee of an outcrop.

Even coming darkness does not warrant hurrying. Beginning the long angling climb that would carry me more than two miles along the length of the ridge and at the same time bring me to the crest, I dropped my pace yet more.

The sky had clouded over, though reserving here and there a patch of blue. Occasionally the wind, scudding the clouds before it out of the west, let the sun through into the valley.

High above the ridges an eagle soared, wings barely moving, catching the westerly wind that was swept upwards half a thousand feet by the slopes against which it rushed in its hurry from the distant sea.

A late ground squirrel took sentinel stance above his burrow in a patch of mountain soil, then, shrilling his alarm in a high-pitched whistle, scurried into the safety of the earth.

The valley floor grew more distant and the skyline of the ridge much closer.

The going was good, as Dave had promised. As the daylight changed to approaching dusk, I could identify the saddle easily from the pitch of the ridge beyond it, readily seen now to be the same saddle I had watched from the northwest when Dave had explained it all in the distance. Just a little, I let myself hurry on, anxious to find Dave at the top, to make shelter against the wind and the night, to seek in his company again the fragile security a man needs when his insignificance is forced upon him by the awesomeness of the mountains, the wind and the sky.

Chapter 42

Dave was not there.

For a moment I thought I must have mistaken the place. But the rise to the south and the massive rocks, reaching another five hundred feet higher toward the leading end of the ridge, made it plain that here was the only pass.

The saddle was wider than I had imagined. Easily a quarter of a mile of flat land lay between the crests of the eastern and western slopes, and on the eastern side to the south a sheltered draw, wooded with stunted evergreens, offered a stringent camp. In a pocket near the western side lay a bit of water held by some odd fold of the mountain strata that trapped a little snow melt, keeping it from hurrying off the slopes in the August sun.

I walked along the western edge in the face of the howling wind, searching down the ragged slopes in the falling darkness, but I saw nothing of Dave's slight figure working up the last of the climb.

I checked an impulse to go a short way down to meet him. It would be wasted effort and after all there really was nothing to worry about. Delayed perhaps by killing a sheep, he knew the slopes enough to come on in the first of darkness. I could be most useful by making camp.

I set myself this task, exploring the wooded draw for its most sheltered spot. I soon discovered it, for others had made their hasty camp here, too. Hard against a wall of rock lay the remains of a leanto frame, a little dried-out brush once used for bedding and the charred ends of campfire wood. Here the wind might almost be excluded, left to whistle around the rocks above.

Before doing anything else, I gathered wood. This lay sparsely where struggling trees had grown to a few feet then died, drying out in the rotless atmosphere of the mountain top. Others had searched here, too, and before I had a pile fit for the night, I had ranged as much as two hundred yards from the camp in what now had grown to be the full dark of night.

My anxiety for Dave edged toward fear. When the wood was gathered I walked again to the western crest, but there was nothing but the suffocation of the wind and the blackness of the slopes below.

On the way back to the campsite I drank from the water, for Dave had the billy and there would be no tea. When I made the leanto, cutting green wood for the frames so I might burn the dried remains of the old frame, I made the shelter only so large as I would need for myself.

There is no longer a night than one spent worrying. Of course, Dave had spent all his life in these valleys and among these mountains. But it had been a long life already, and the sureness of foot that had served so well must someday fail.

Perhaps I should have suggested, even insisted that we keep together. Dave would have agreed. He'd wanted us to approach the camp from separate sides because that doubled the chance of shooting sheep. But surely I might have weighed safety against the extra chance of killing sheep and decided in favor of safety. We had plenty of meat in camp now, down on the banks of the Yukon.

I put off lighting the fire and making my rough bed. I improved the shelter, feeling about in the darkness, and ate sparingly of the grub I had left in my pack, wondering if Dave, too, ate of his.

Whatever had delayed him, would he have a bivouac of sorts somewhere down on that slope? Would there be brush and fuel? Water?

Very late, I lit a small fire, close to my bed, piling a semi-circle of rocks on the offside to trap the heat.

Then I rolled up loosely in the canvas, my arms free, one to rest my head, the other to reach for the sticks I would feed slowly to the fire throughout the night, one or two at a time, just enough for a tiny blaze to keep me warm in the short snatches of sleep by which, at best, I would pass the time.

234

Should I not have gone at once down the western slope when I found Dave wasn't here? Logically not, of course, if nothing had happened, for in that case he would have arrived as he had planned, at dark or a little after.

But something had happened, there was no other explanation. If I had only struck off down the slope at once, firing my rifle for a signal, he would have fired his in answer and I should have found him, eventually. Then, whatever else, we would have been together. Or would we?

Perhaps I slept, though I was sure I didn't. The wind blew unabated, whistling relentlessly against the ragged surface of the rocks. Occasionally I tended the fire; occasionally I shifted in my canvas to relieve the discomfort of the ground beneath me; occasionally I conjured Dave out of the fantasy of my half sleep, only to wake fully again and listen to the wind, knowing how harshly it must be striking on the exposure of the western slope.

Chapter 43

In the dark of morning I sat before the fire with the canvas over my shoulders, rationing out the last of the wood against the chill. I ate what remained of my food, standing occasionally to stretch out the stiffness, squatting again soon for the meager benefit of the fire, wishing for daylight.

When finally first light crept up the eastern sky I had abandoned my camp and shouldered my packboard, taking up an impatient position on the crest of the slope, walking back and forth for warmth, trying to will away the last of the darkness.

Slowly the ground immediately below took shape, then, in turn, the distant floor of the valley. I could begin to make out more than had been clear on my arrival the night before. The steepness of the slope left much of it hidden from sight: what I could see was rough. To the north below the main outcrop lay, as far as I could see, a slope of rock fragment and wiry, twisted scrub, the roots grasping for life somewhere down below the boulders, into the sparse pockets of soil. Somewhere, in the approach, a man must cross that, the footing treacherous, the wiry knee-high brush dragging at his legs.

With daylight full, I started down in short, deliberate drops, stopping as every new stretch of ground came into view to search the rocks.

On the third leg down, perhaps a hundred yards below the saddle and a little to the north of it, I stopped on a bench of rock that gave a wide view of the rubble to my right, and the first of a thin line of spruce a mile or more away to the left and far below.

Instinctively, before raising the binoculars, I scanned in a full circle, above as well as below.

236

You never expect the wild ram. Suddenly he is there and your breath is taken. Almost all white this one, almost pure Dahl on an intergrading range, he stood frozen against the rocks beneath the outcrop a hundred and fifty yards above.

The curled horns, massive against the head, spiraled outward in a graceful sweep that framed the startled eyes, the face held high.

There was time to shoot, but I did not unshoulder my rifle. I had no time for anything now but joining Dave, and if I found him well, delayed only by miscalculation and darkness, I should simply ask his forgiveness for letting the sheep escape.

Shortly, the ram caught my scent in a shift of the upward wind and bolted from sight. I turned back to my urgent search.

As I worked down, I avoided going into the worst of the rubble, staying along its edge, searching it by eye as I went, trying to estimate from my growing view of the valley where Dave would have intersected it and had to cross.

I debated about firing signal shots. I had twenty rounds of ammunition: five in the magazine, one in the chamber, fourteen in a belt pouch. I could spare three for one signal, but how often might I signal before a reply? And what interpretation would Dave put on the shooting? How many rounds might he have to make replies? Would he hear anything anyway, the wind tearing the sound off up the slope?

I put the idea aside for the time, continuing downward, working to the left now as my interest grew in the distant stand of spruce.

Reaching an outcrop that gave a good view, I settled, elbows on knees, and applied the binoculars to studying the ground and the line of timber.

Nothing out of the ordinary. Just a fringe of trees in a draw where there might possibly, though not likely, be water. Odd that there should be enough protection for timber to grow there, in the full teeth of the westerlies. Nourishing pocket of soil perhaps.

And suddenly I grew painfully despondent. It seemed so long ago that Dave had been beside me, sharing tea by the stream in the bottom of the main valley below the confluence. For the first time, I consciously admitted the thought of tragedy, of Dave stumbling in a critical way in the failing light, lying unprotected through the night in the unmerciful wind.

I forced the thought away, the consequences too inevitable. But Dave, warm and alive beside me, was harder to imagine than before the thought had grown.

Suddenly, where there had been nothing, I saw smoke. It rose in billows out of the spruce timber, then, caught by the wind, it swept away into nothing.

It was no campfire. It was a signal, deliberately put up in enough volume to be seen before the wind destroyed it, and long enough after daybreak to let me come part way down the slope where I'd have a chance to see it.

I jumped up and ran toward it, then stopped as I stumbled in the awkward footing. Then I stood a while and laughed out loud, the tension ebbing away, the foolishness of my first response so clear.

I wondered if I should shoot, then decided it had little point. Dave might yet not hear the shot in the wind and I would join him none the sooner for it.

Most of a mile lay between me and the spruce stand and I crossed it slowly, the footing deteriorating again as I neared it. When Dave had said it was poor going on this side, he'd been making his usual understatement.

The smoke diminished, then disappeared. No doubt Dave planned to send it up in intervals, rather than waste effort making it continuously.

I walked into the timber, which grew in a distinct draw and much more substantially than I had thought, at exactly the place Dave must have come in the night before. Through the first of the trees, I shouted and he replied.

Past a thicket of smaller trees I found him, lying on a mat of spruce boughs, with a generous fire going, and still a few sticks of dry wood in reserve beside his leanto. I had wanted to find him so badly I felt embarrassed now, as though he knew my feelings.

"What happened?"

"I turn my foot in them rocks."

238

His boots were off, and I could see the swollen ankle. I dropped to my knees to look at it, then realized there was little to be learned by doing so. "You had a tough time making camp."

"Not bad. It happens before dark. But I can't climb mountain then. I make camp quick. He's sore, but he's not stiff till morning. I can walk on him last night, but I can't walk on him this morning."

He had a comfortable camp. His leanto was a little sparse, but he had plenty of boughs beneath him and his canvas folded over him would break the last of the wind. He had much more fire than I'd had on top of the ridge.

But I thought of food and wished I hadn't eaten mine and could offer it him now. And water. "You got any water here?"

"There's little swampy place below. You can just fill billycan."

"You got any tea left?"

"Little bit."

"I'll get some water."

I found the place and brought back a billy full. Then I gathered more wood and soon we had the water boiling.

Over the tea, I confessed about the ram, finishing with an apology, explaining my anxiety about him as best I could. It sounded a weak excuse now we were together and Dave's ankle would be fit for walking in a day or two at most. In fact we needed grub, and now I'd have to walk down to our main camp to fetch some.

But I reckoned without Dave.

"Good thing you don't shoot. I kill sheep last night and we can't pack 'em both."

"Good shot! Where did you kill? Far from here?"

"Just I comin' across rough ground, he comin' up same place. I kill him. That's when I turn my foot. Too much hurry to get where he's down. I scared I don't hit him right and maybe he's goin' to get up 'n run."

"You must have killed him well before dark."

"I got lots daylight left. I gut him out and I got time to walk to top of mountain, but my foot he's gettin' stiff 'n I know I got to make camp."

I poured the last of the tea into Dave's mug, then swished the leaves out beside the fire. "You explain where you left him, I'll go pack him in."

"You go straight to bad rocky place. Don't go up, don't go down. You see my glove on end of stick I stand him up."

"Okay. And don't try walking around on that foot. Give it time to get better. You try to use it, you'll make it worse and we'll have to stay all winter."

Dave grinned his "I've got a joke" kind of grin. "You eat some sheep meat, you like to stay all winter."

I found the sheep with no difficulty. It was a young animal, and the fat was evident in the offal and along the slit into the cavity.

I skinned the carcass, slowly, for chilled hide comes less easily than warm and I wished to avoid any contact of hair to meat. Then I severed the neck and halved the carcass across, leaving two ribs in the hind half, making pieces I could lash to my packboard and carry easily to camp in two trips.

I made the first pack in then and spent a little time fetching fire-wood before going back for the rest of the meat.

After the second trip and when all the meat was hung in camp, I felt hungry enough to eat sheep meat raw, but I put off doing anything about it in the remaining daylight. While I'd come off the ridge at daybreak and found Dave fairly early, the greater part of the day had been used up, and I hankered for a comfortable night.

You take no rest in a poor camp so I set to making a good one; but first I fashioned Dave a pair of crutches.

These are easily made. You cut a straight green stick about two inches in diameter and the length of the desired crutch, then bind the last six inches of the small end.

Then you carefully split the stick from the large end, all the way to the bound section. All that remains is to insert a six-inch spreader between the split halves at hand level and again at the top, lashing the uprights hard against the spreaders.

The moment Dave had them he was hopping about the camp, dragging in dry sticks for the fire and spruce boughs for bedding by holding them between the bend of his elbow and the uprights of the crutches.

By dark we had a well-brushed leanto facing the fire from either

240

side and a thick mattress of the softer boughs in each leanto. At the head end of the shelter lay a heap of firewood to last easily the night and half the following day.

Then we pursued the other comfort of our mountain bivouac. We had both that morning finished the grub we'd brought, and the day had been demanding. And while we made out on the river and the trail when necessary on bannock and beans, rice and tinned bully beef, we were really meat eaters, given to entire meals on large chunks of moose or caribou, aided only by the ubiquitous tea of the woodsman. I felt so hungry my hands shook, and it was meat hunger all the way. I did not need to ask Dave if he felt the same, only which piece of mutton he planned on first.

Sitting on his spruce brush with his tender ankle out in front beside the fire, he built the blaze up against the early darkness.

I knelt opposite, absorbing the warmth of the fire into my weariness, a happy weariness, the better to rest for having it.

"Ribs?"

"I think so. Cut him right across 'n then split him on backbone. We hang him on stick."

I went to the fore half of the meat and cut between the ribs from both sides to the backbone, taking several ribs on each side, up to the tender end of the shoulder blade. Then I broke through the backbone with the axe and brought the piece to the fire where, by its light, I split the vertebrae. Now we had a set of ribs apiece.

Next I cut two green sticks six feet long, sharpening both ends. One end I rammed obliquely into the ground, leaving the other pointing to the fire and about a foot away from it. Then I cut short stakes to prop the stick up so it would bear the weight of the meat.

"Look about right?" I wondered if Dave might not have done it differently.

If so, it didn't show. Maybe, like me, he was so full of the idea of eating the meat, he wasn't fussy how we cooked it. He nodded approval and I impaled each set of ribs on its stick, heavy end down, meat to the fire, rib bones away from it.

We fed our fire with dry willow, a little at a time, keeping the meat hot yet never burning it, letting the heat seep slowly in and through.

The fat lay evenly over the meat and in layers through it: it glistened now in the firelight and soon began to drip. After a bit, the coals spilling out from the fire reached the drips of grease and little licks of flame shot up occasionally, searing the thicker meat along the backbone.

The smell of the cooking meat, rich and promising, mingled with the wood smoke. I looked from the meat to Dave's bronze face, the shifting light framing him against the poles and boughs of the shelter behind. You could easily imagine his face had got its color from the generations of his people who had stared into open fires at night and weathered the smoke in their eyes, however unscientific the notion.

Gradually, the glistening fat grew crisp and the exposed red meat turned brown. Everywhere, the roasts ran with juice and grease. It seeped from the knife-cut ends, running in little streams down the browning surfaces.

Finally, when for the third time I put the back of my hand against the ribs on the far side of the meat from the fire, I could feel the heat, uncomfortably hot, all the way through. Done. Hot, juice laden, tender and cooked but not one whit too much.

"You ready?"

"I starve to death I wait five more minute." And Dave pointed his knife to the sticks he'd laid on the ground before him, on which I then dropped his chunk of meat. Skillfully, he sliced a piece free with his knife, speared it on the point, blew on it gently, then took it from his knife with his teeth.

"You like that?"

"Mm," he managed past the piece of meat, "he's good."

So I swung mine away from the fire to stop it cooking and, using my own knife in the same fashion, sliced a chunk nearly free, stabbed it, tore it the rest of the way, then ate it from the knife point.

Dave had killed the best of sheep, and sheep is the best of meat. The hot, tender slices disappeared one by one until, long after hunger had gone, even when discomfort had set in, we still picked the bones for flavor.

When we could do no more with the meat we settled back to sip

242

the strong black tea. How different this night was from the one before on the mountain top.

I confessed to Dave my terrible anxiety when he had failed to meet me, and how I'd been up early waiting for daylight, wishing the night would go so I could start my downward search.

And what about Dave? Had he been fretful in the night, worried about our being separated, thinking perhaps it had been wiser if we'd hunted together even though we'd cover less ground?

"Oh, I'm not worry. If I'm all alone, I'm in hell of a fix. Maybe I'm not get outa here. But I know you goin' look for me in morning and you goin' see my smoke. I just sleep till it's time to put up smoke."

Whereupon I wondered whom had I really been anxious for last night on top of the mountain in the howling wind, Dave or me. Or us both at once in the loneliness that turns men for solace to each other.

When there are only two in half a thousand miles of wilderness, there is but one link between a man and all mankind.

Chapter 44

We stayed two more days, eating heavily of the sheep meat while we waited for Dave's ankle to lose its soreness.

Before we left, I cut the bones out of the remaining meat, ending up with no more than a load for my own packboard. Dave traveled light, lessening the chance that he might cripple up again, forcing us into another camp.

I fretted some about our main camp on the Yukon and the possibility of a cranky grizzly going through, ripping up whatever he could and strewing our meat all over the surrounding bush.

"Oh, he be all right. Maybe grizzly up on mountain yet." Which was to say, let's worry about the things we can help, and never mind the things we can't.

We broke out at first light the morning we left. Breakfast was a reheat of meat cooked the night before, but we'd run out of tea and the meal lost a little of the leisurely quality of our food taking.

"What's the most important thing the whiteman brought to the Indian, Dave?" I asked facetiously as he chewed the meat all by itself.

"Tea," he replied, knowing we both missed it as much.

"If I asked you that in the spring when the snow is wet, you'd say rubber boots."

He spat a piece of gristle into the fire. "One time I make fire with rubbing stick, like my uncle show me long time back. That time, it's matches."

"And if you met this sheep we're eating beyond arrow-shot and no gun, it would be guns."

Dave tossed a clean bone into the flames. "Indian now, he wouldn't know how to live old way. He don't want to live old

244

way, too. It must be tough way to live. Whiteman brings all kinds stuff makes easier for Indian to make his life in bush."

I wondered if Dave was done, and after a silence he said the other half.

"But whiteman brings trouble, too. Indian can't stand drink. He gets in town, he can't make it. He drinks 'n he can't keep job. Indian made for bush, not for job in town. But he stay in town 'n pretty soon he's no good for bush, too."

It was the most I'd ever heard from Dave on the subject and maybe it summarized all there was to say. As if to end it in any case, Dave scattered the fire, spilling on a billy of water to quench the last of it, and we both reached for packboard and rifle.

The trip back took till dark but the worst was over after we'd picked our way through the rough where Dave had turned his ankle several days before.

The camp was unmolested and by morning we were fully rested. Now we might turn back to our main journey.

"What next, Dave?"

"That cow meat dry now. We pull out tomorrow, early."

The weather held cool, tops for keeping meat. My quarters of bull moose had nicely blackened with surface drying and they'd keep a couple of weeks, maybe right into winter frost, before they would need to be stored in a deep-freeze back in Whitehorse.

So really the trip was over. We had our meat, we'd had our days of river freedom, and we'd plied the side channels of Dave's memories and the stories of his people.

"How many days, here to Dawson City?"

"Three days we paddle hard. Four days we take it easy. Maybe we goin' kill one more moose. We see."

Fine with me. I had the bull the law allowed me. What Dave took according to his way of looking at it was his business.

We took to the river again.

Now that the cow meat had dried, the canoe had plenty of freeboard once more and we paddled in earnest, happy to hear the silt against the canoe skin again, to watch the banks slip by, to choose the channels between the islands and smell the river sloughs on the sharp fall air.

245

We camped that night half a day's travel upriver of the Stewart River mouth, and the following day at noon we passed the old Hudson's Bay post there.

We next camped on a bar at the mouth of the Sixty Mile River. There on an island, only a rifle shot across the westerly channel of the Yukon, lay the remnants of the buildings that once had been Ogilvie. Here, those many years ago, Ladue had run his store and sawmill when the gold of the Sixty Mile was as exciting as anything the Yukon offered. Here, Henderson had arrived, dejected and ready to quit and had been inspired to prospect in one more try, on the Indian River, from whence he had crossed into the drainage of the Klondike, not to strike himself, but to tip off the squaw man, Carmack, who, with his Indian companions, turned Rabbit Creek into the world-famous Bonanza.

Here, in fact, Carmack must have stopped on his downstream journey to the mouth of the Klondike where, in early August of 1896, he had engaged in nothing more world-shaking than drying salmon and swatting mosquitoes and blackflies.

But on this night the mouth of the Sixty Mile belonged to us, as indeed did the island where Ogilvie once stood, and all the Yukon from the Klondike to the mouth of the Stewart. We lay on our bedding in the candlelight, listening to the swish of the river and the intermittent slap of the canvas on the teepee poles as the wind rose to an occasional westerly gust.

"One more day to Dawson City, Dave?"

"Long day."

"Let's stay here tomorrow. I like this place. I camp here every time I come down the Yukon. Maybe we kill you another moose."

"Okay. 'N we camp near Indian River, too, if we don't make it here. Good camp there 'n good place for moose."

"Don't those guys from Dawson hunt Indian River pretty heavy? Only a short run with an outboard from town to the mouth."

"Oh, they hunt him all right. But they don't bother him much. Not them boys from town."

I could see his point. Too much town makes a poor hunter out of a man, all right. Oh well, it was all the same to me, and I was too sleepy to give it further thought.

246

The next morning we scouted the bottomland around the lower reaches of the Sixty Mile. Two bulls had squared off, then churned the sand of the stream bar to a mass of tracks as they fought.

"You like to kill one of those bulls?" We studied the sand, estimating the fight as two days old, maybe three.

"He'll do. But he's getting late for killing bull. I like to kill cow again I think. Bull, he's getting strong."

I didn't bother to crawl through all the labyrinths of that again. If Dave wanted a cow, we'd shoot a cow.

We climbed a steep slope to a high bench to the south that gave us a splendid view up the Sixty Mile valley and up and down the Yukon for many miles, as well as of every open patch in the spruce and willow of the bottomland. At our feet the dung of wintering moose lay thick on the ground, and everywhere the willow was trimmed by browsing.

"Moosey, isn't it?"

Dave grunted his agreement as he settled on a windfall to study the view. I took up a comfortable station overlooking a different part of the bottomland, and we settled down to several hours of wordless companionship, sharing the possibility of a kill and the cheery idleness of nothing better to do than wait for it.

I slept at times, my jacket drawn against the wind, and doubtless Dave did, too. Long after noon had passed, I said that I was hungry.

"We go back to camp. Moose not goin' to move aroun' now till almost he's dark. We try again when he's start to make dark."

Stiff from sitting, we let ourselves slowly down the slope, then picked our way along the game trails out to the river's edge and the bar where we'd camped.

Sheep meat, almost the last of it, and bannock went down with the tea, and then we passed a few more hours lying about the camp, occasionally fetching wood or fixing a bit of gear.

"Dave, we're going to get lazy if we keep this up much longer."

Dave stretched and lay back on his bedding again. "Now we take it easy, maybe later we kill moose, we got lots work to do."

Another difference between whitemen and Indians, maybe.

Whitemen have this fixed notion that work is a virtue and that being horizontal in daylight is some kind of sin. Indians never quite acquire that notion and invite all kinds of negative judgments from whitemen when they content themselves with doing nothing when there's nothing to do. All in how you look at it, really.

With the last hour and a half of daylight, we made a diligent search again of the Sixty Mile mouth, climbing once more onto the bench land to the south.

But no luck. Finally, we trudged back to camp just as the light began to fail, resigned to pulling out in the morning to hunt the Indian River country.

I don't know who saw her first, but we both became suddenly aware of her as we stood by the teepee looking across at the island and the overgrown site of Ogilvie.

"Cow!"

"You look with you binocular."

I was already looking. She was a big cow, and there was no sign of a calf. She mooched about along a clear piece of bank, and there'd have been no reason for her calf not to be out with her in plain sight if she'd had one. She paid us not the least attention.

But it wasn't all that ready-made. The shot was too far and the light was too poor for Dave's carbine; only my .270 with the telescope, from a securely rested position, would make the kill—but of course it could, with no room for doubt.

We both knew that, so I put up the remaining problem. "How the devil do we get her over here after we kill her? This current is running pretty fast."

Dave had that figured. "We take empty canoe 'n we walk him upstream far as we can this side. Then we paddle him some more in slow water close to shore. When we cross, we go like hell 'n we come out on island pretty near bottom end of island, but we make it."

I got the picture. "Then we walk the canoe up along that tangled, overgrown cutbank over there in the dark, and if we don't drown ourselves, we'll get to that moose and we'll gut her out in the dark, cut her up and load her in the canoe and pretty near drown ourselves hand-lining the canoe up the island to the top end till we can paddle like hell and get back here."

We would be cutting it fine, at that. Going all the way to the upstream end of the island before setting out, we'd be lucky to hit the bank we were camped on above the Sixty Mile mouth; and much below that, hand-lining would be impossible along the rock cliffs. It was a half day's work Dave was talking about, tough work and most of it was going to be done in the dark, feeling our way along the riverbank and inside a moose's belly, as it were. Was it worth it? Maybe there'd be something easier at Indian River.

"Oh, we goin' have hard time, all right," Dave said, reading my thoughts. "But we been lazy like Indian all day, so now we goin' to work hard like whiteman all night."

I could make out the grin Dave spared me whenever he made a joke, and while I enjoyed that he took advantage of me.

"Just my brother takes his big rifle 'n shoots me that moose before he's too dark, then we goin' paddle like hell."

I removed my jacket and rolled it up to make a rest for the rifle. This shot had to count.

For my brother.